LARGE PRINT

Brilliant Dot-to-Dot

GEORGINA McDONALD

ARCTURUS

ARCTURUS

This edition published in 2018 by Arcturus Publishing Limited
26/27 Bickels Yard, 151–153 Bermondsey Street,
London SE1 3HA

ISBN: 978-1-78428-586-9
CH005509NT
Supplier 29, Date 1217, Print run 6926

Printed in China

INTRODUCTION

People express their creativity in different ways. Some prefer the calm and quiet of knitting by the fire or reading on the beach and others crave the excitement of driving a fast sports car or belting out a rock ballad on an electric guitar, but dot-to-dots can be a wonderfully relaxing creative outlet, too, and with such a vast range of creative subjects to choose from, this book has something for everyone.

One of the ways that this book differs from other dot-to-dot books is that it offers bigger dots and bigger numbers so you don't have to strain your eyes to find your next dot. The larger print format means that this book will make a great introduction to the hobby, a wonderful gift for someone with diminished eyesight, or just a relaxing pastime for those who are tired of searching for teeny-tiny dots!

The process is quite simple: just join each numbered dot to the next, in ascending order, to gradually reveal the image. Finding the starting dot is all part of the fun. There are 124 large-print dot-to-dot puzzles each made up of between 150 to 200 dots and the illustrations have been made a little bit trickier than your run-of-the-mill dot-to-dot, with giant gaps that spread across the page (I recommend using a ruler) and images that are hard to decipher from the dots alone. If you find yourself still puzzling over your images, there is no shame in having a look at the image list at the back of the book.

Each one showcases different ways of being creative. From famous singers such as David Bowie and recognizable landmarks like the Leaning Tower of Pisa to sports such as American football and ballroom dancing, you'll find plenty of iconic imagery to inspire no matter how you choose to indulge your creative side!

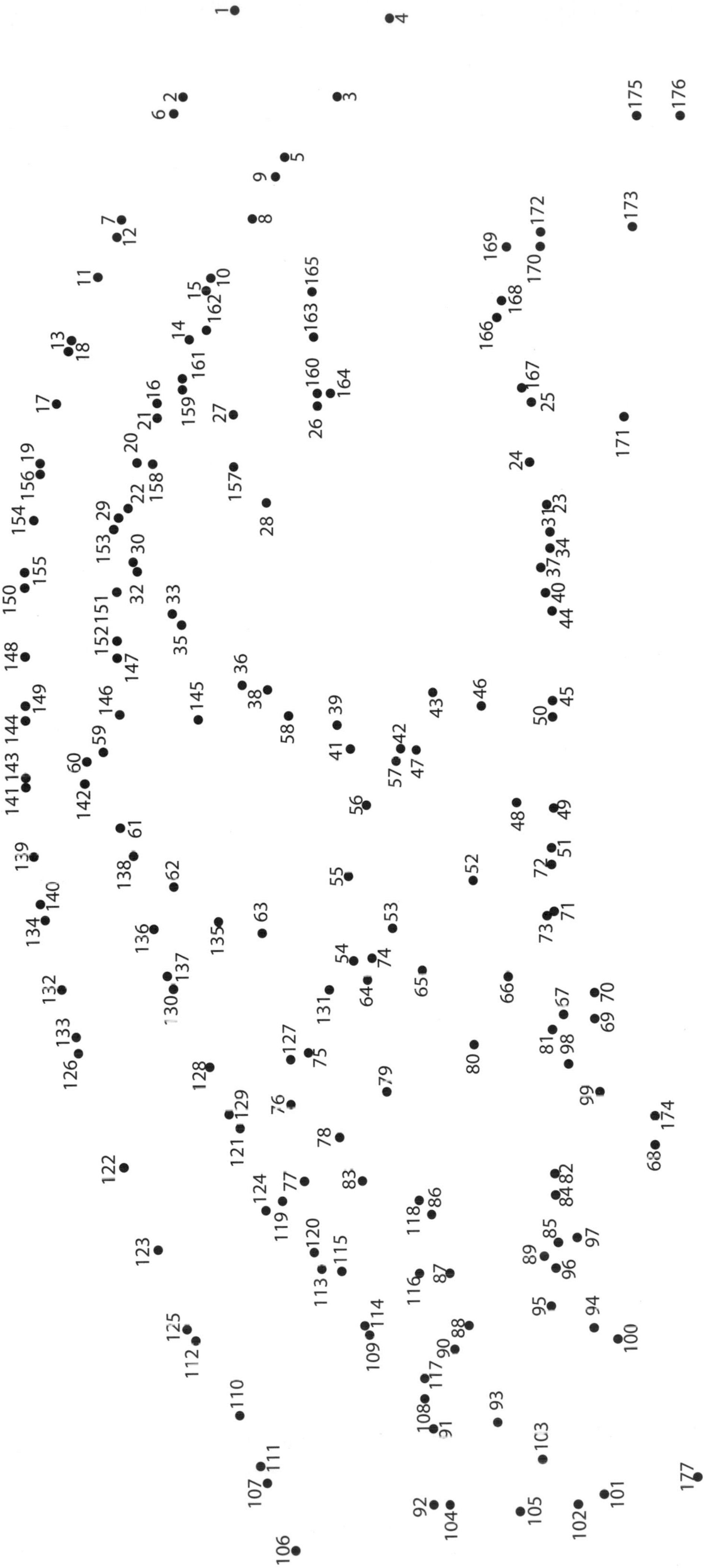

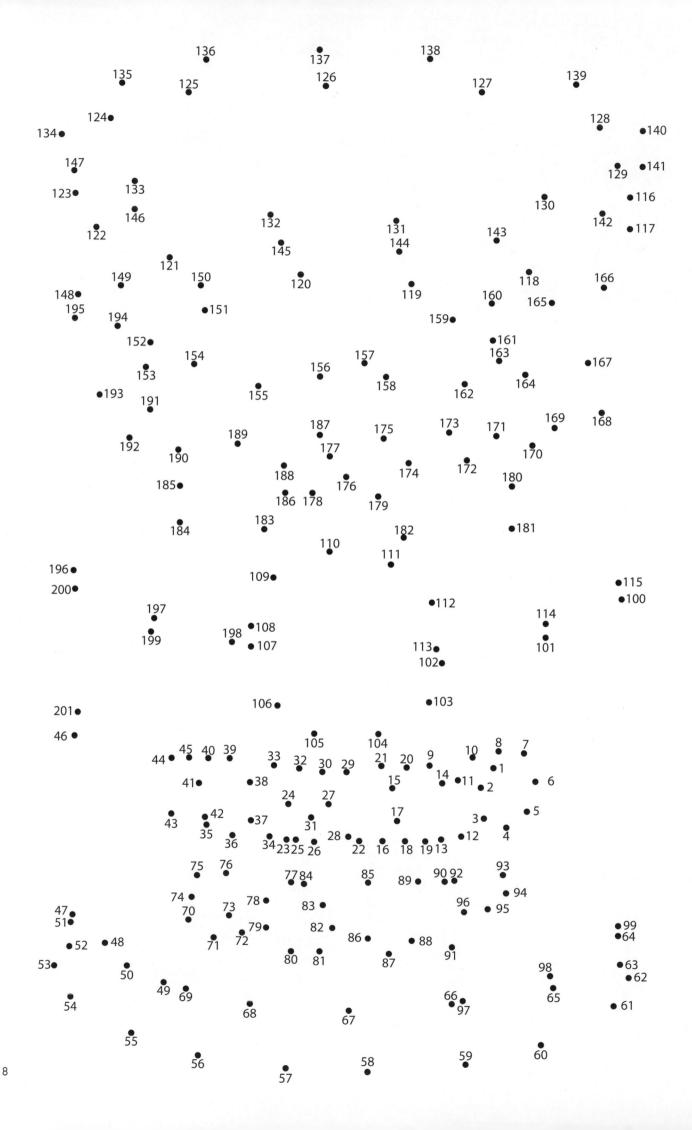

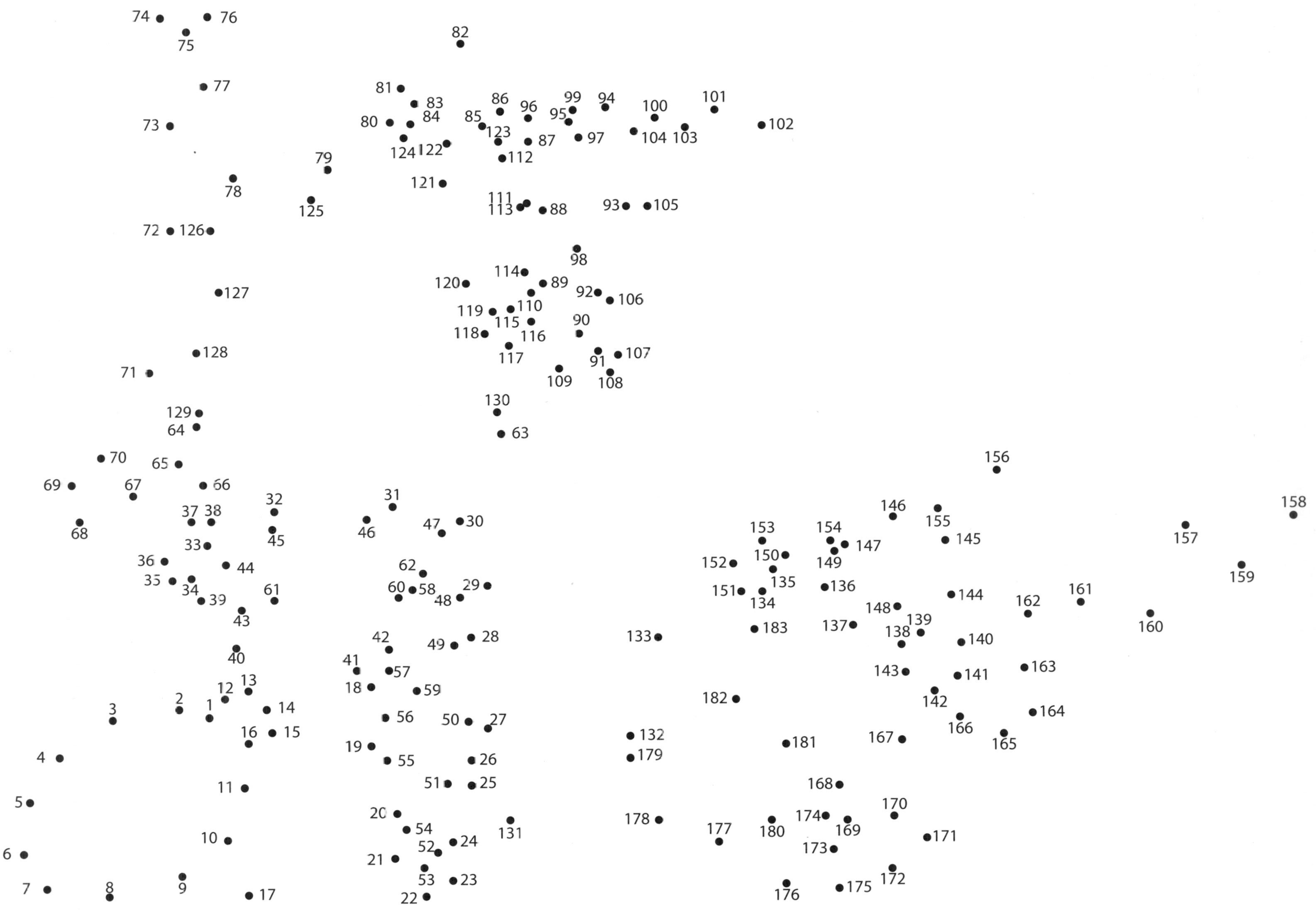

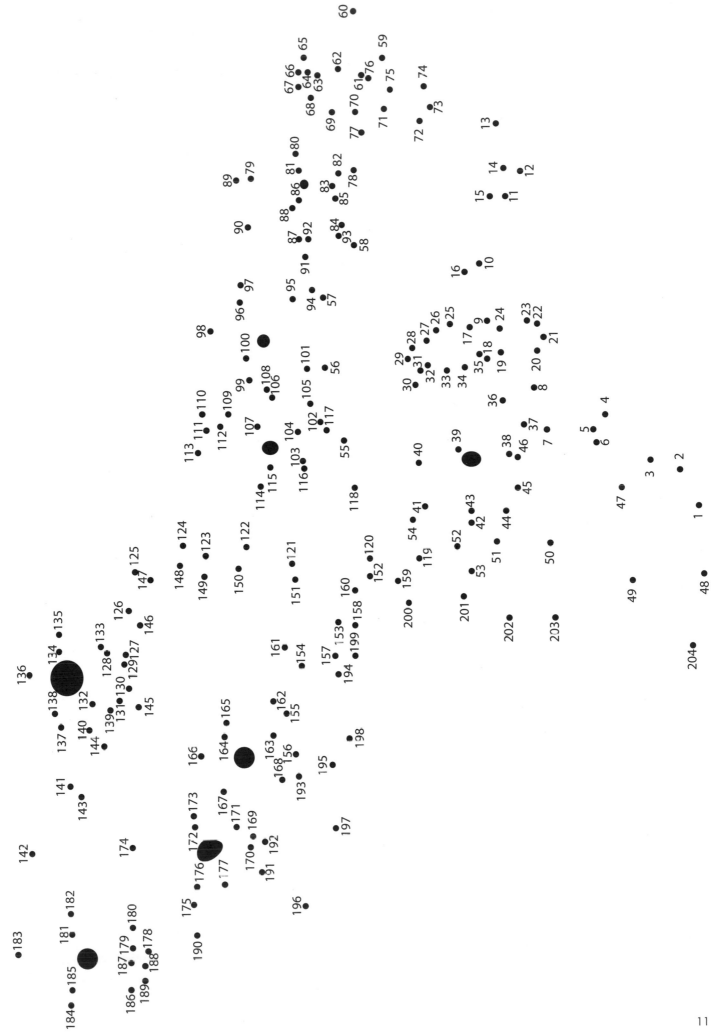

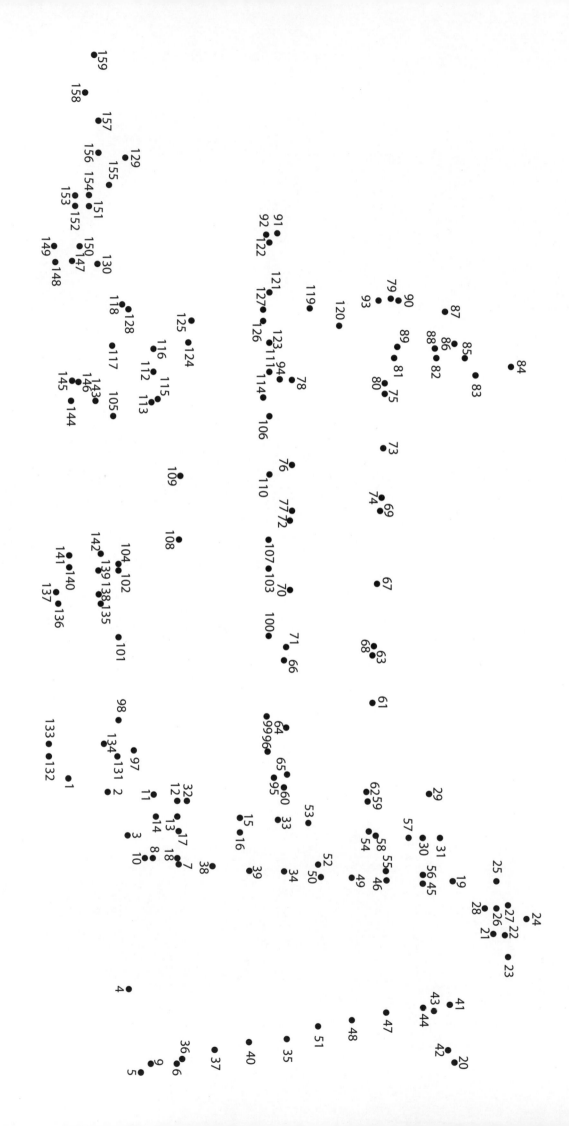

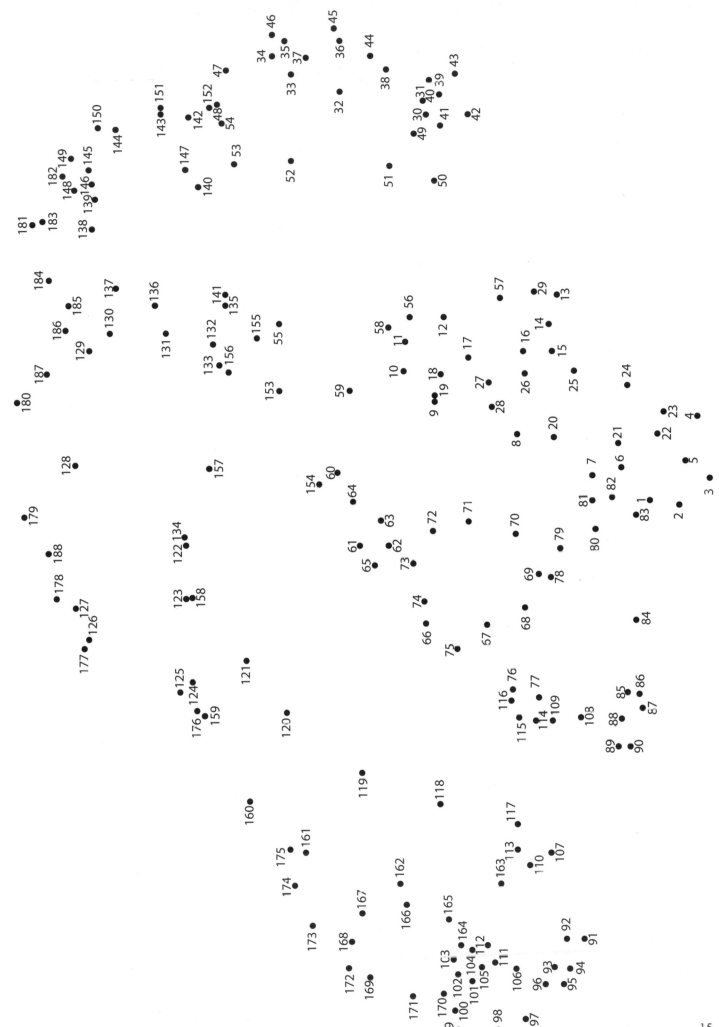

15

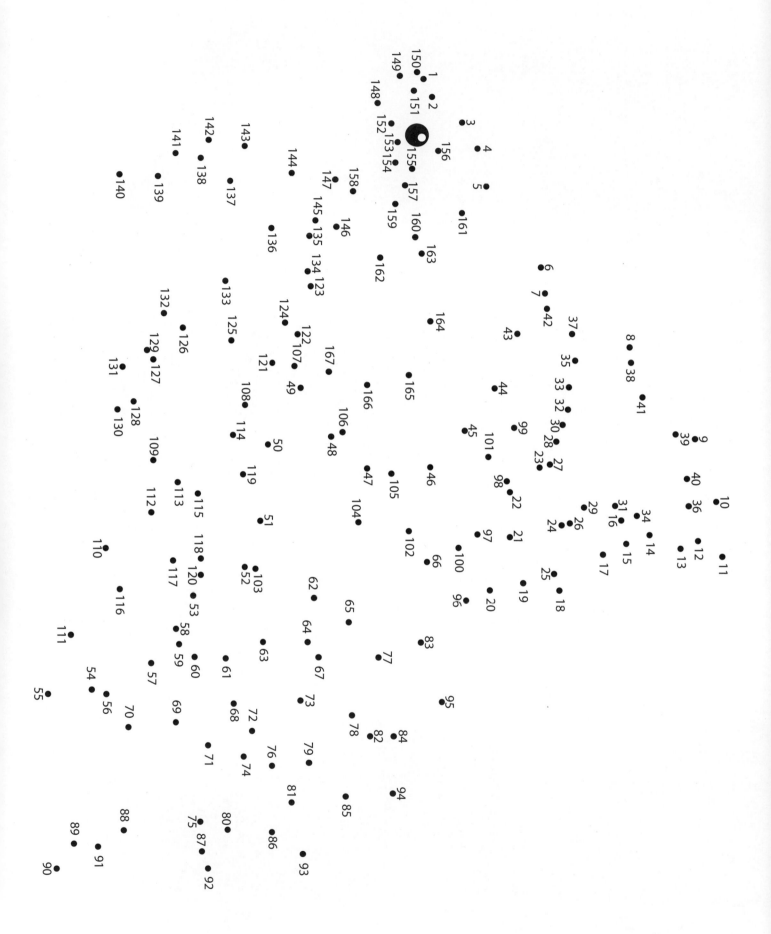

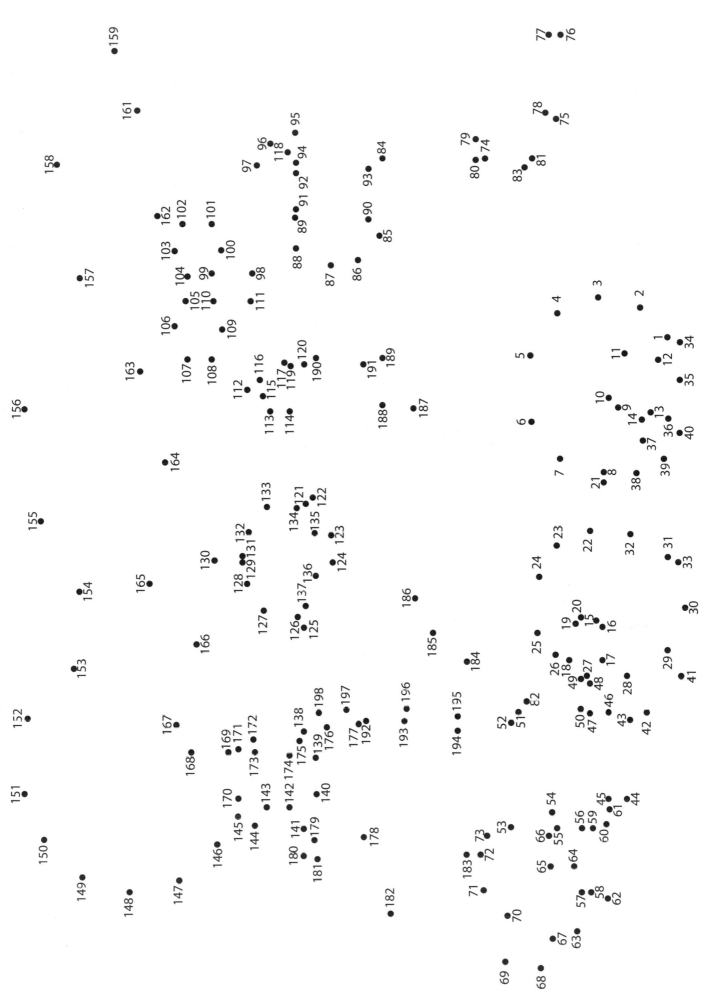

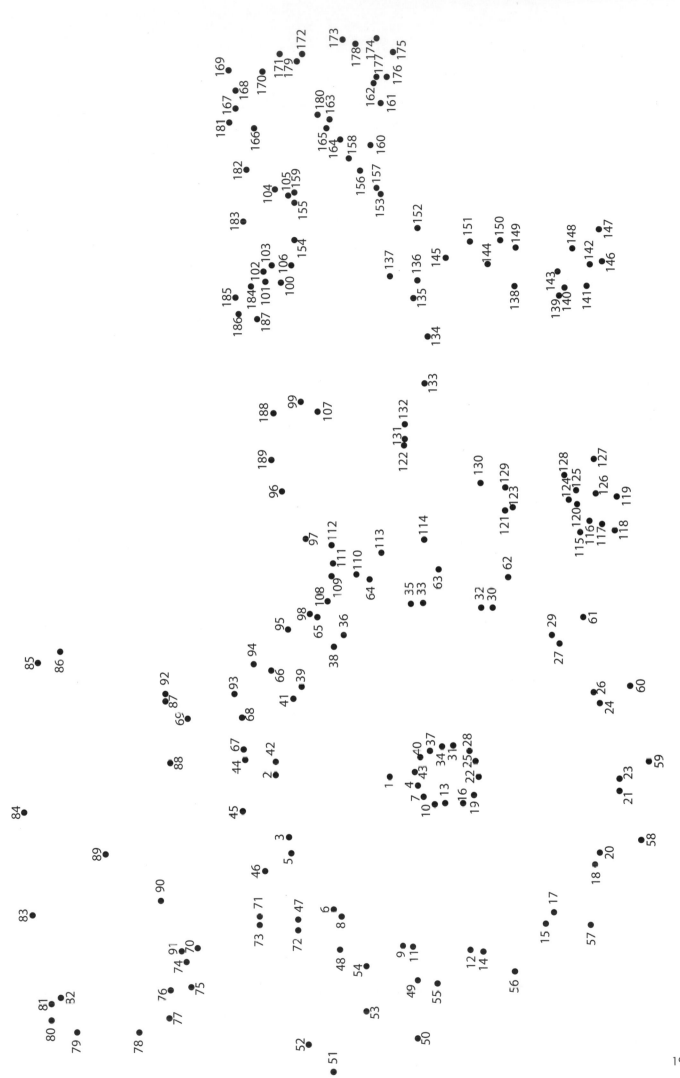

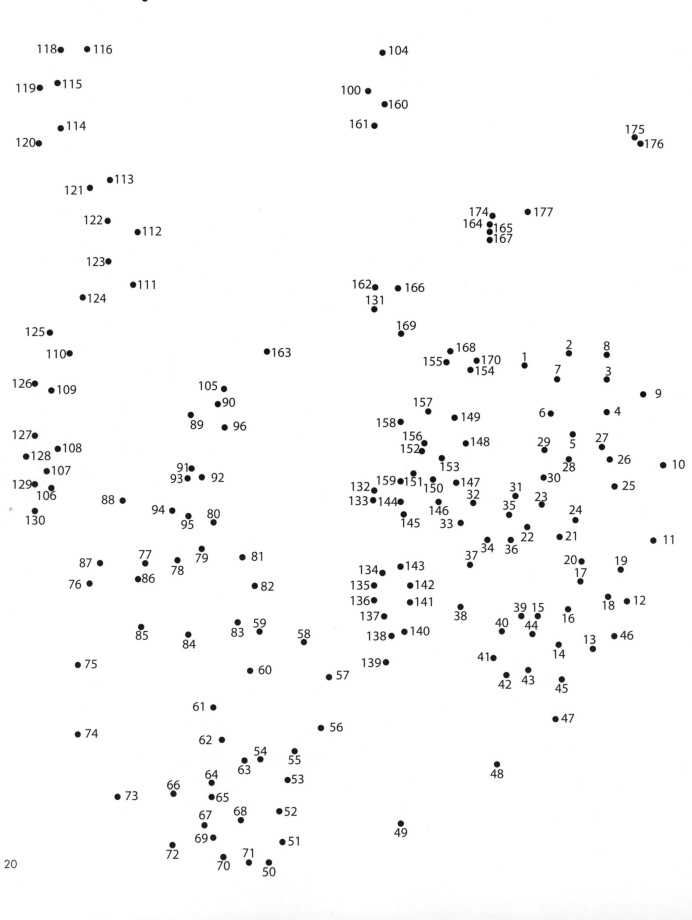

20

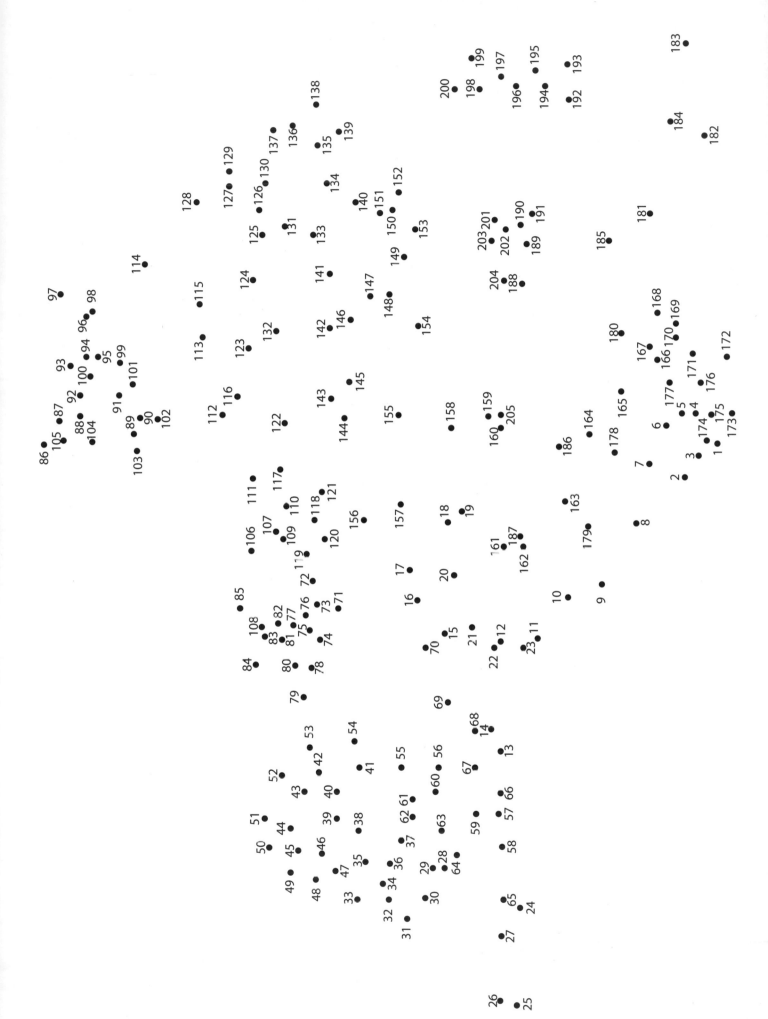

22

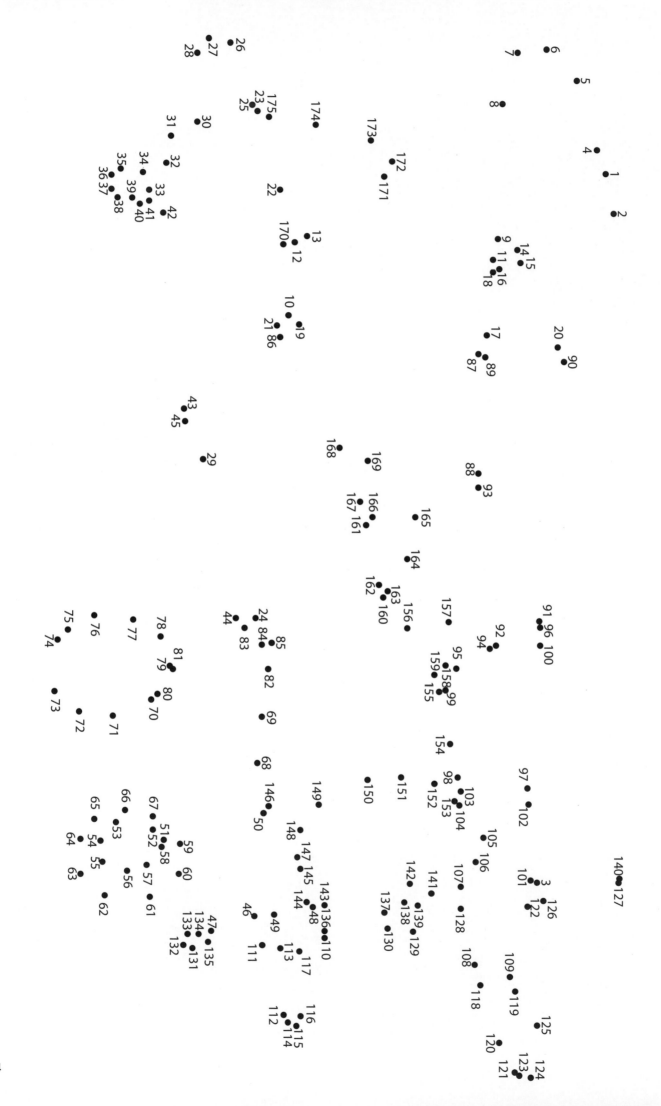

24

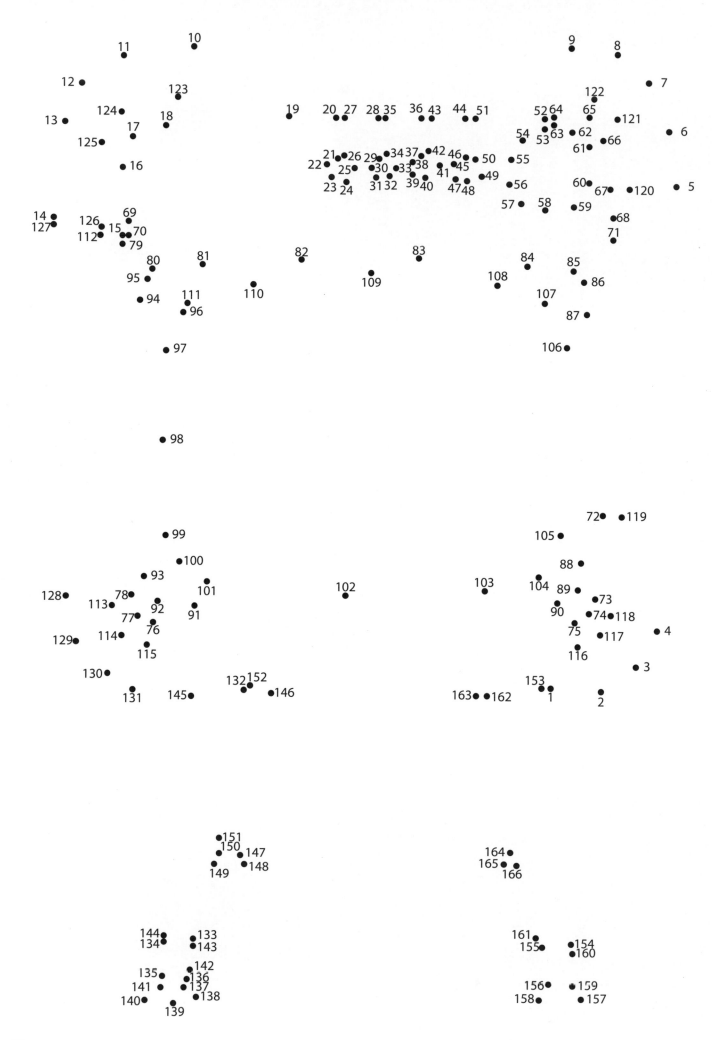

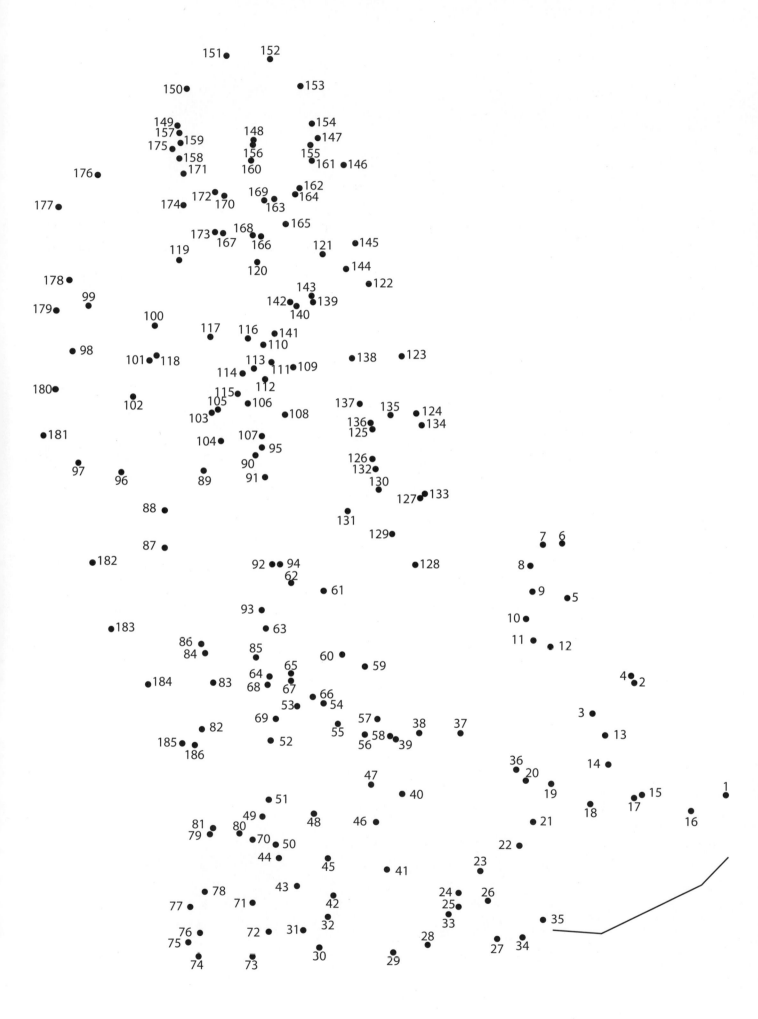

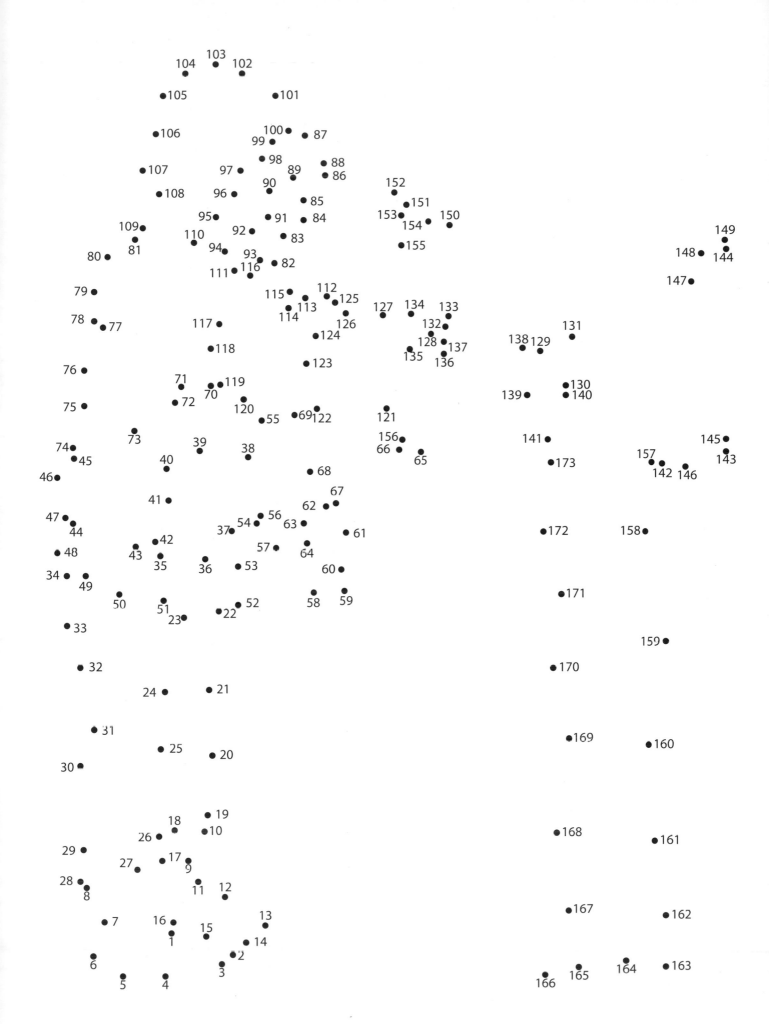

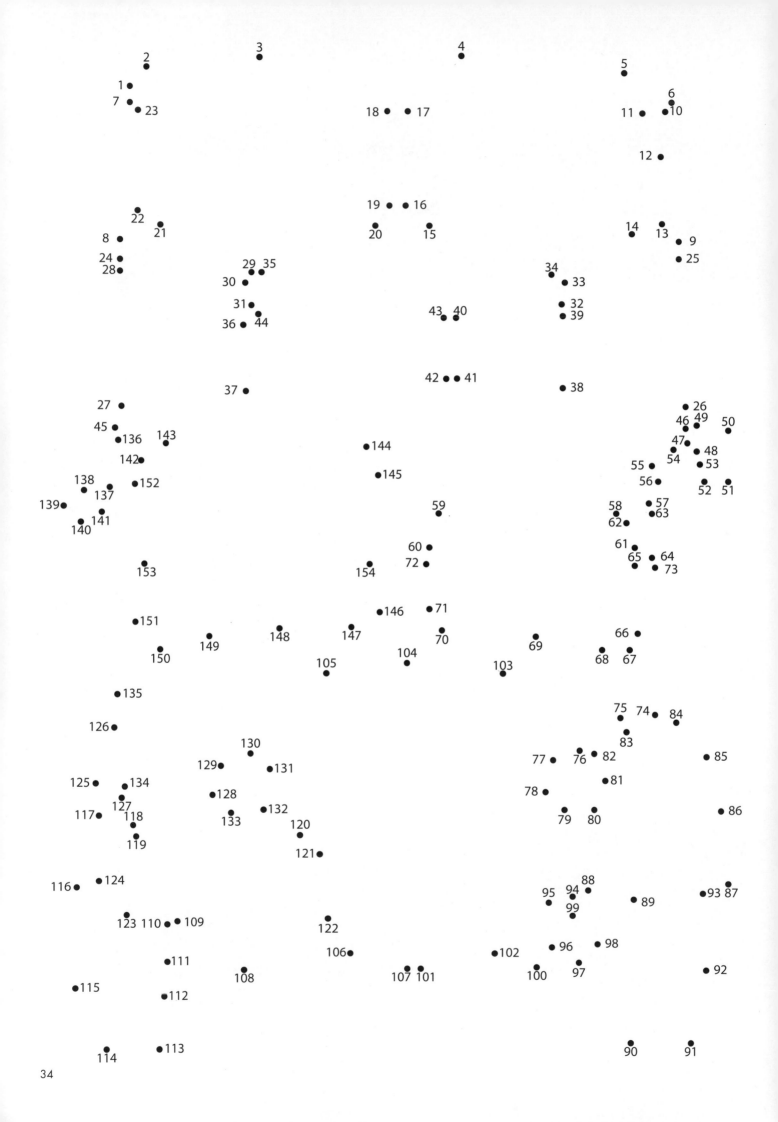

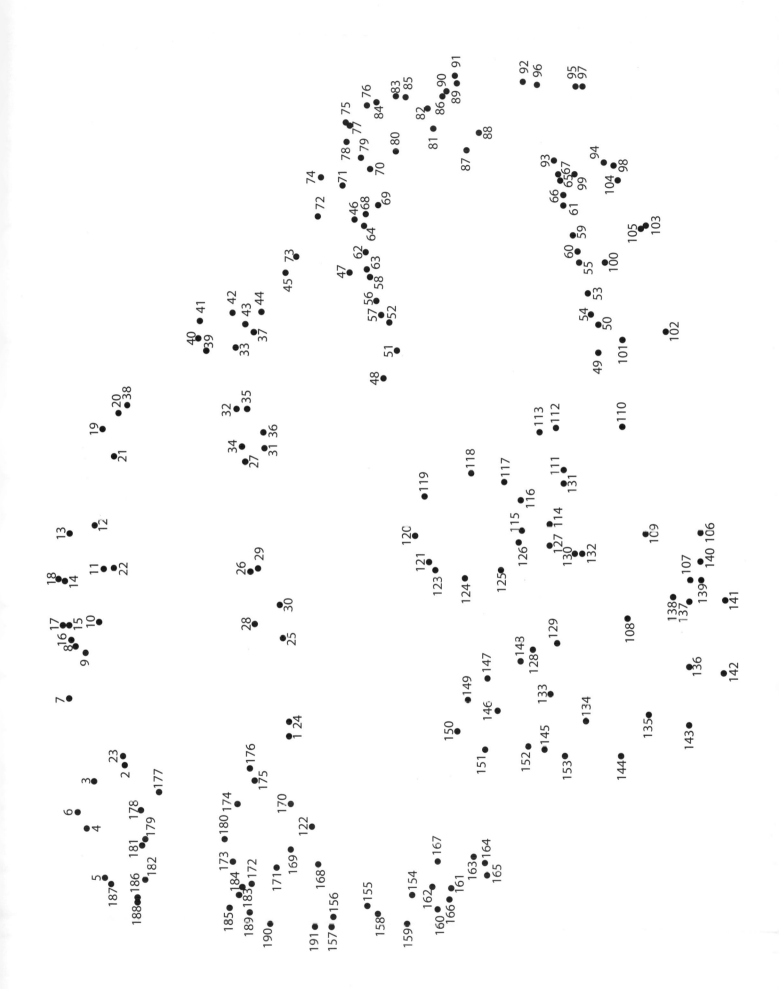

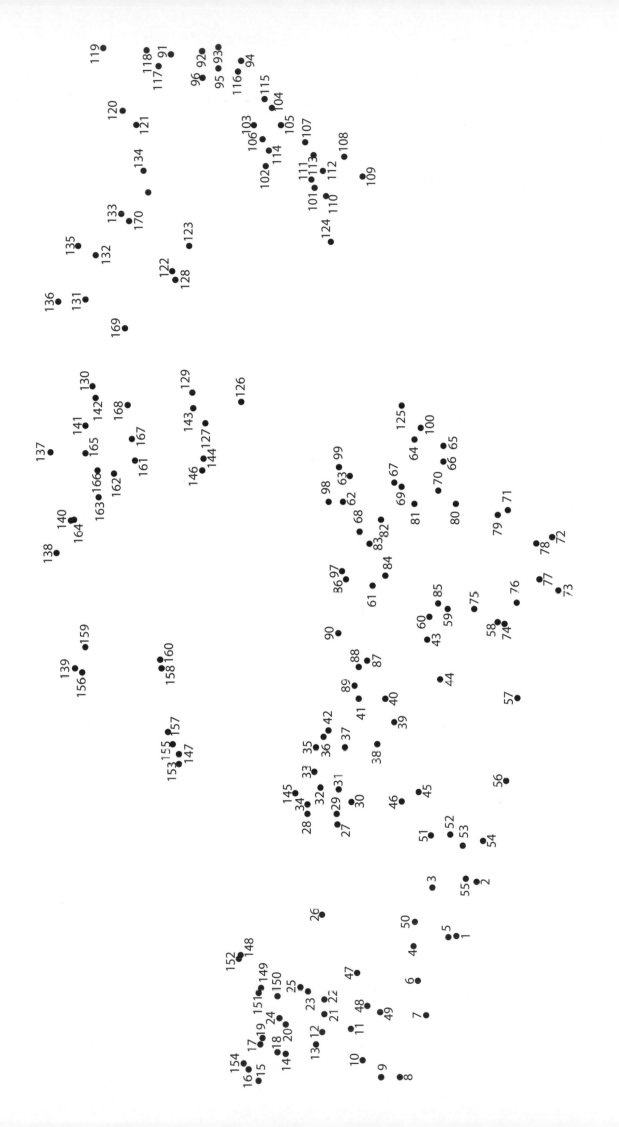

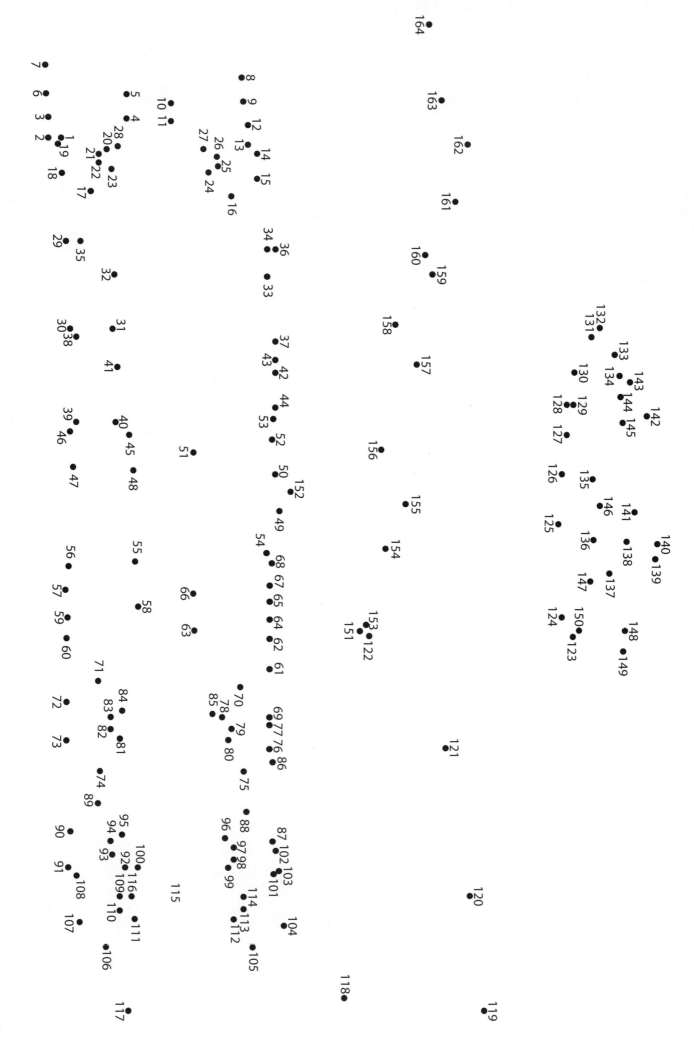

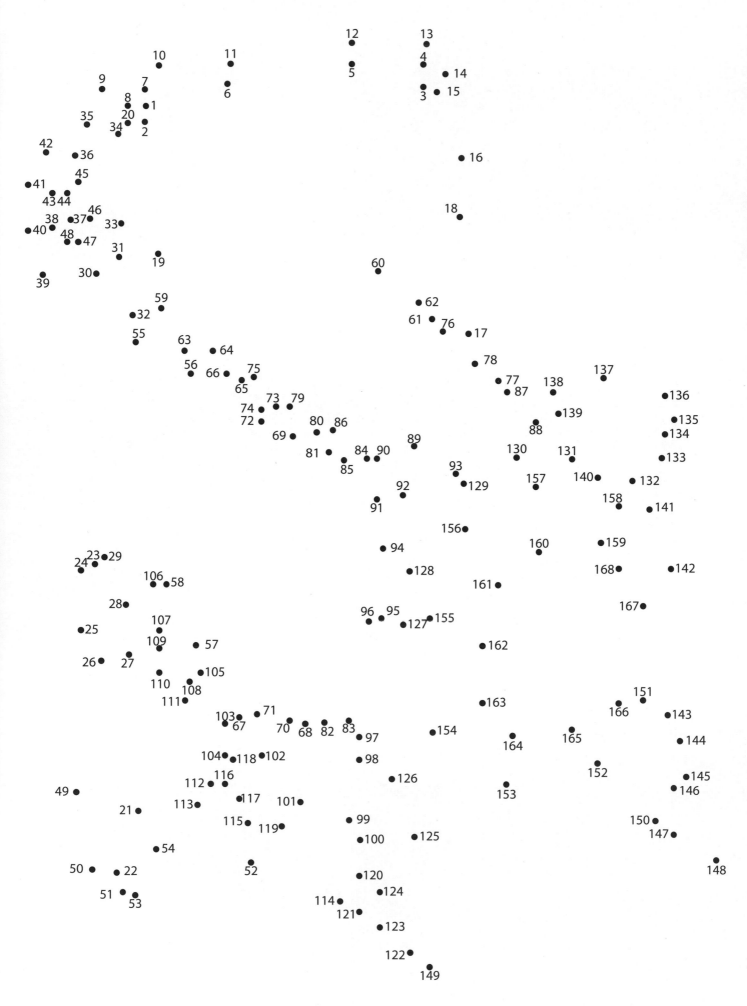

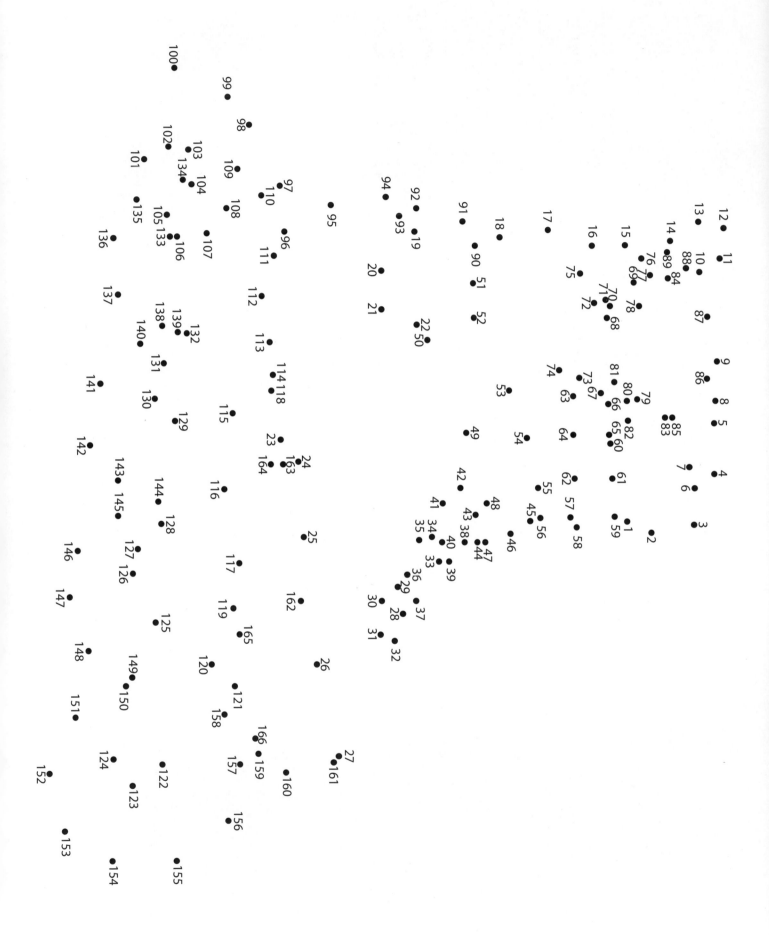

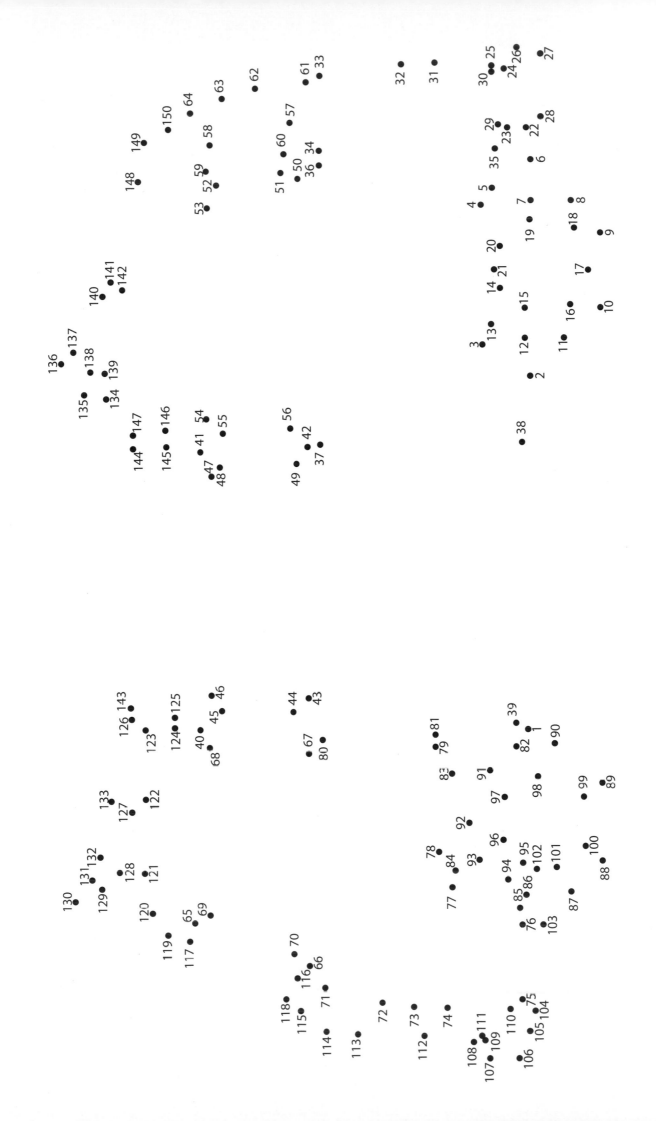

44

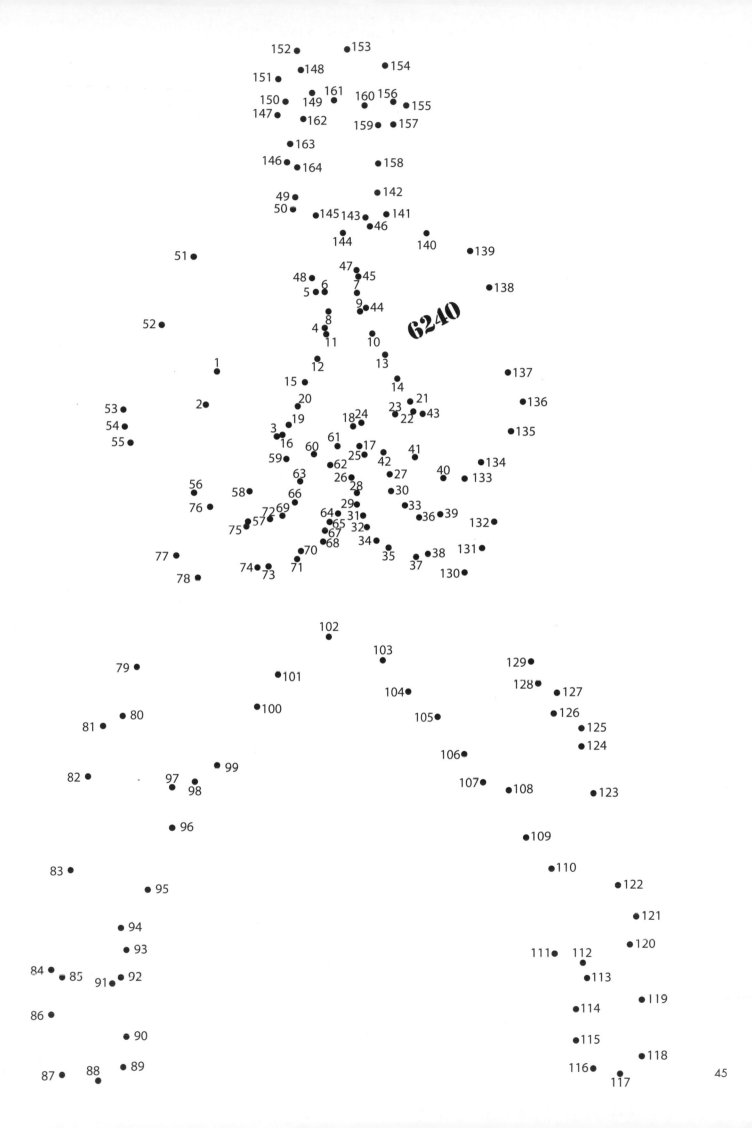

6240

45

46

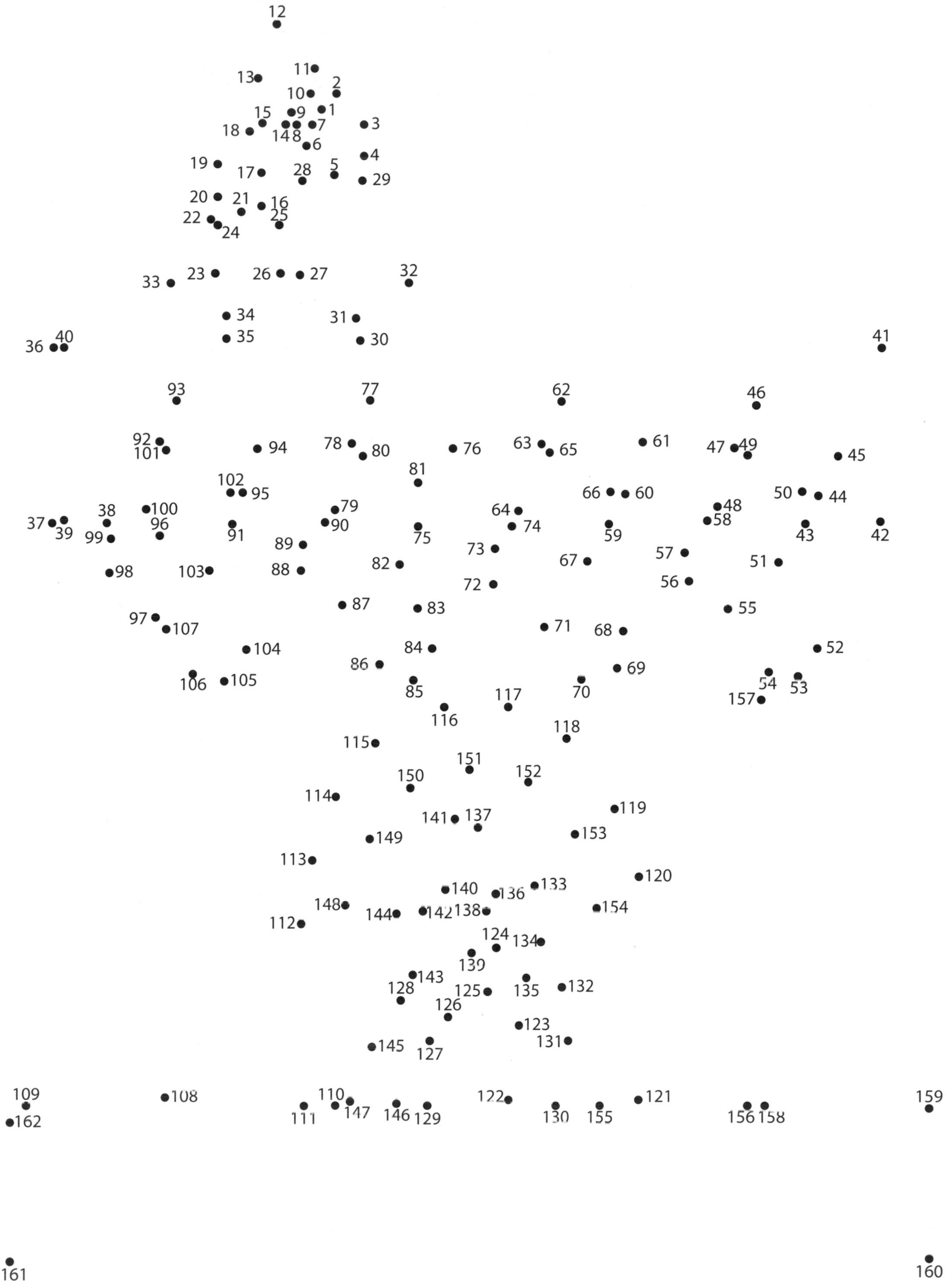

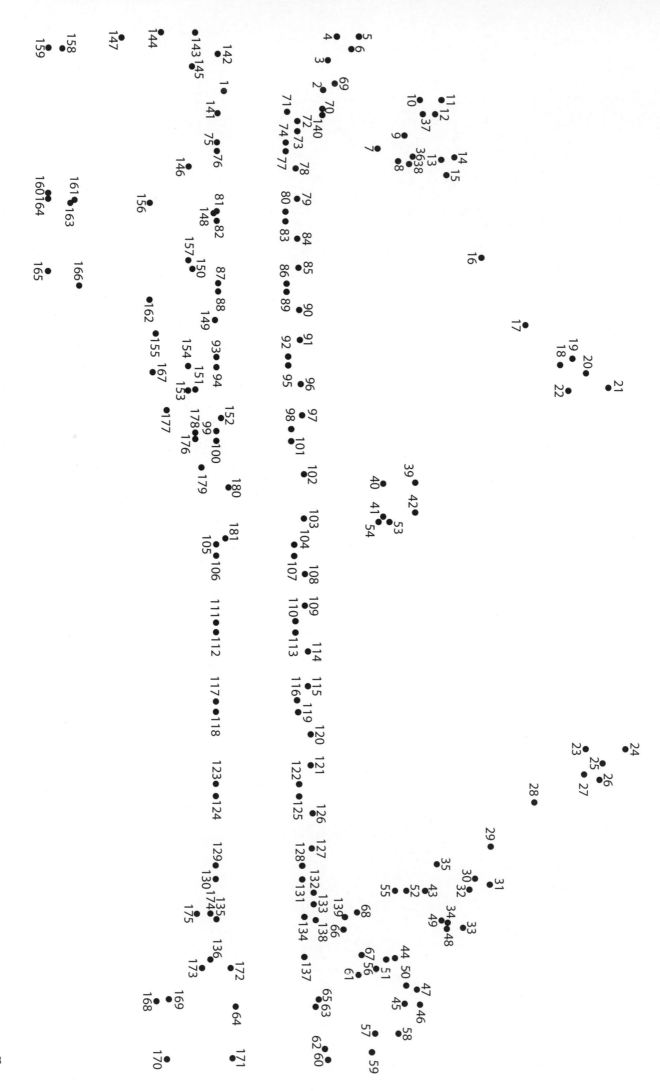

48

50

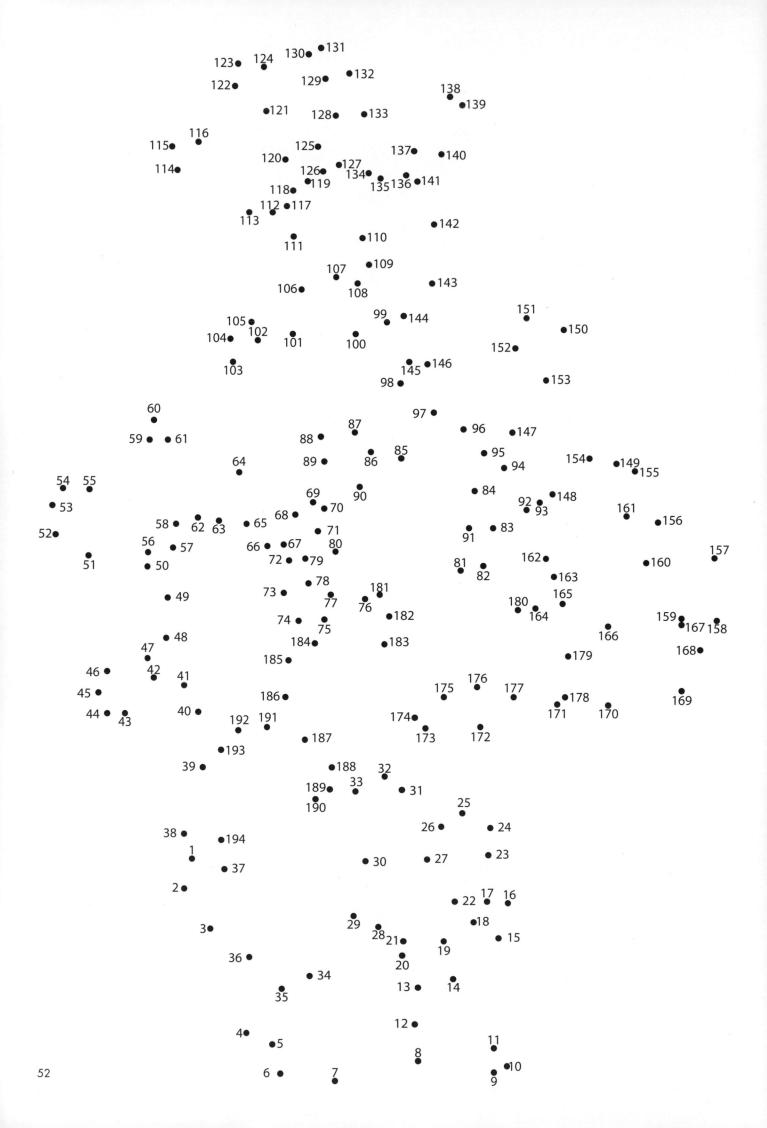

52

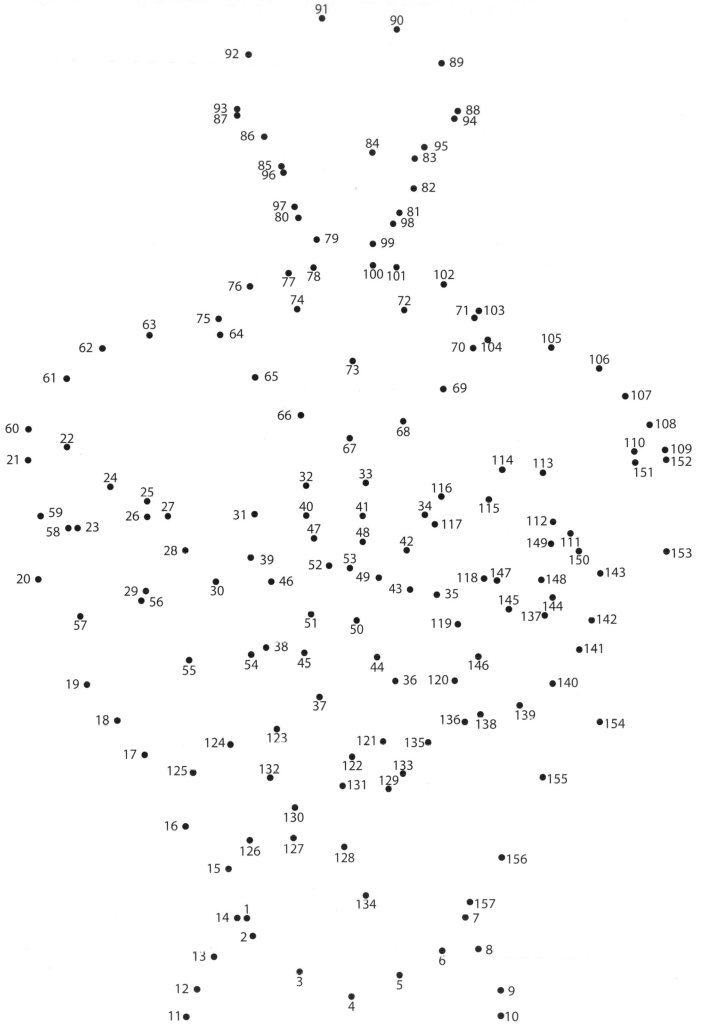

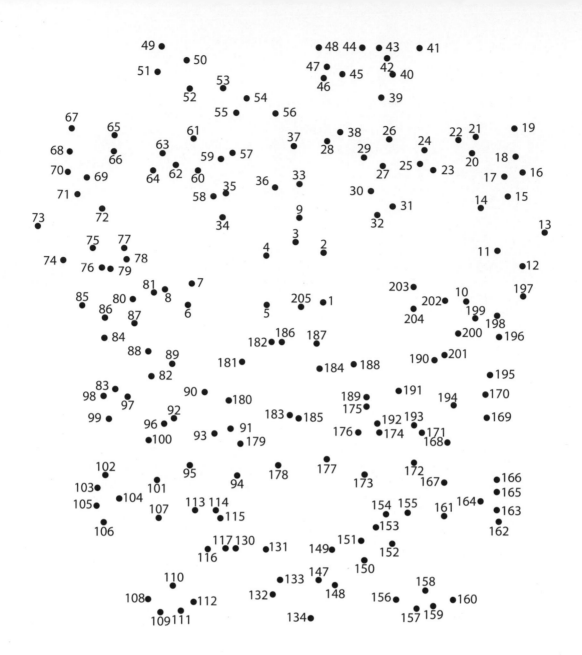
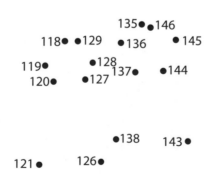

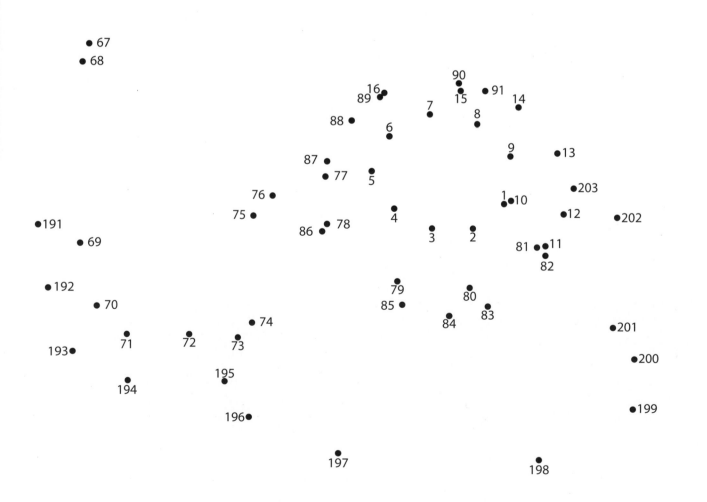

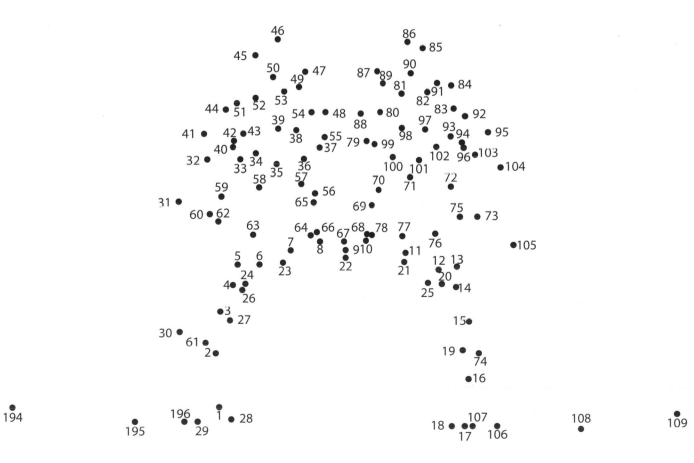

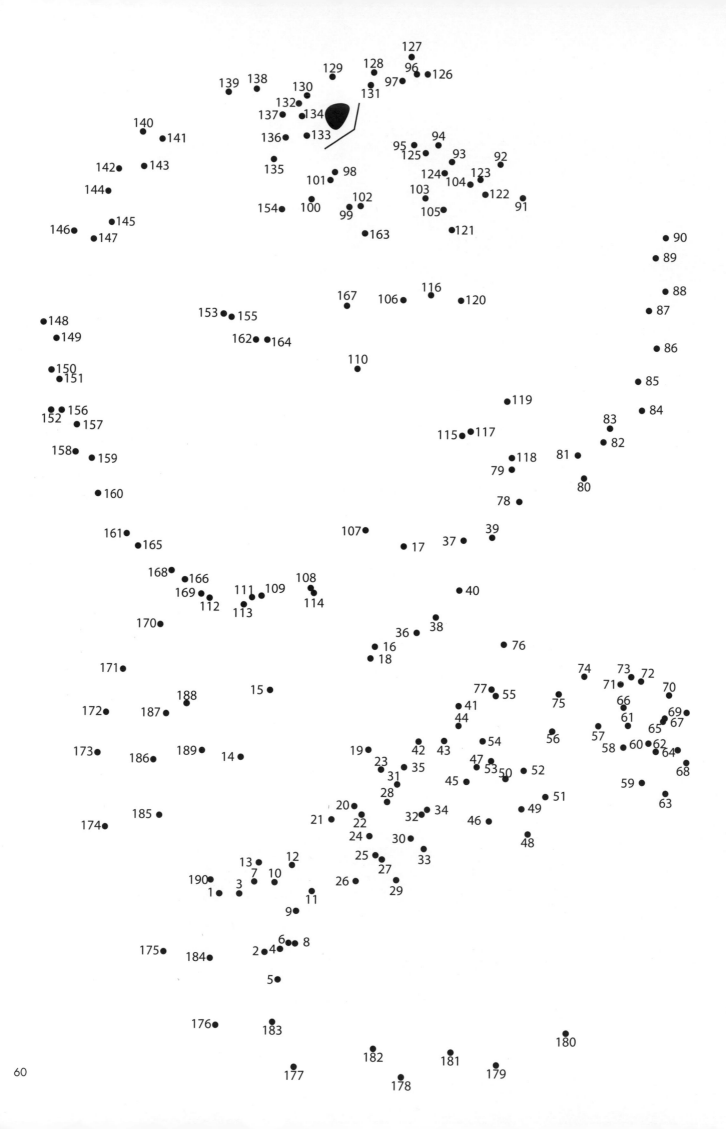

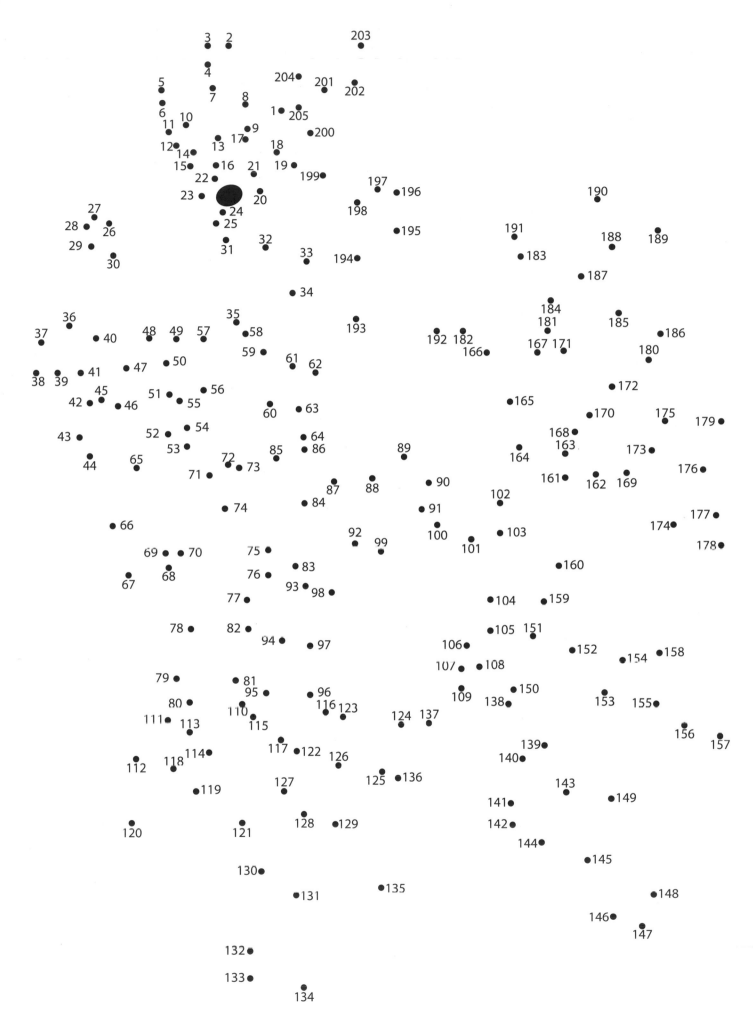

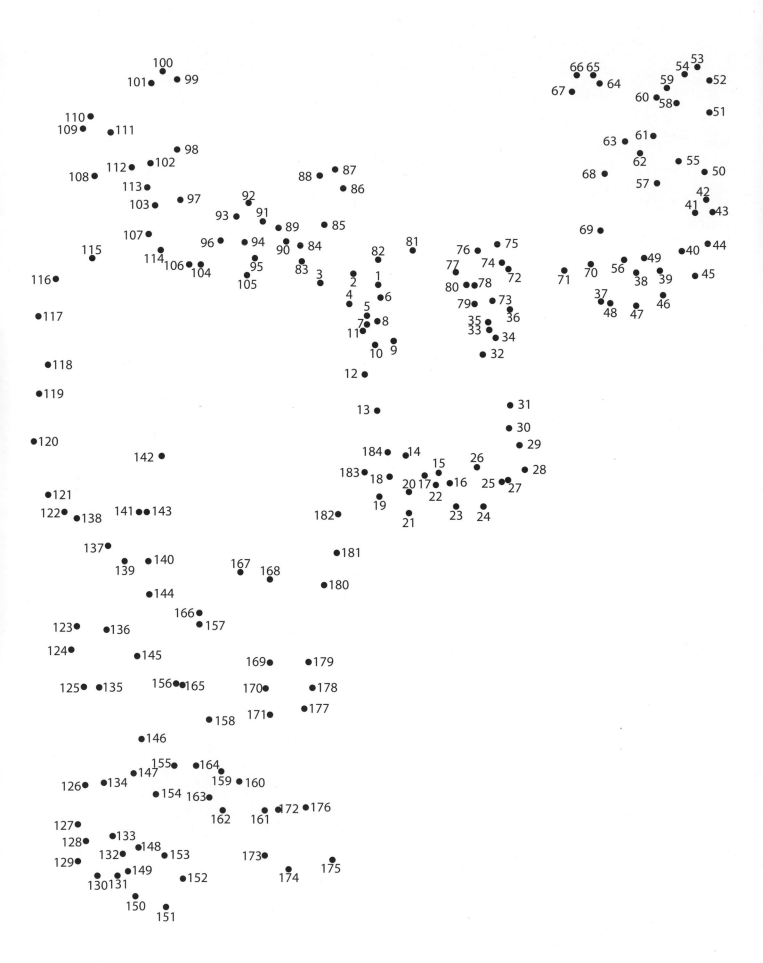

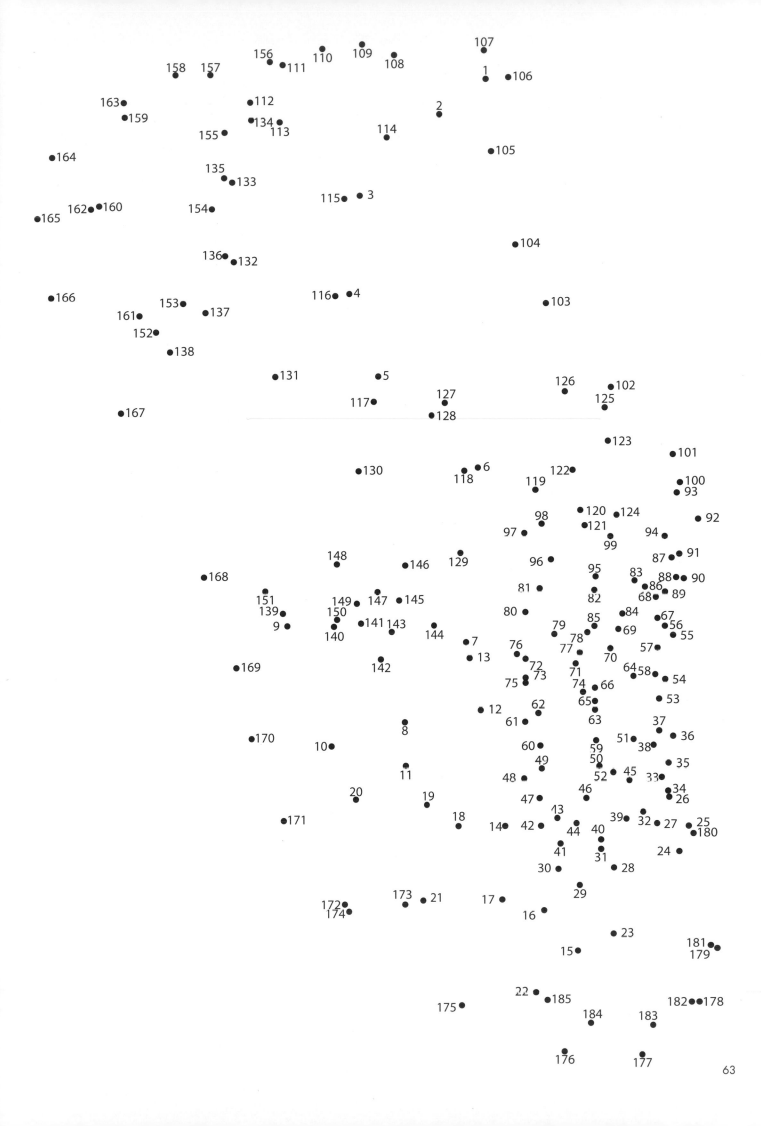

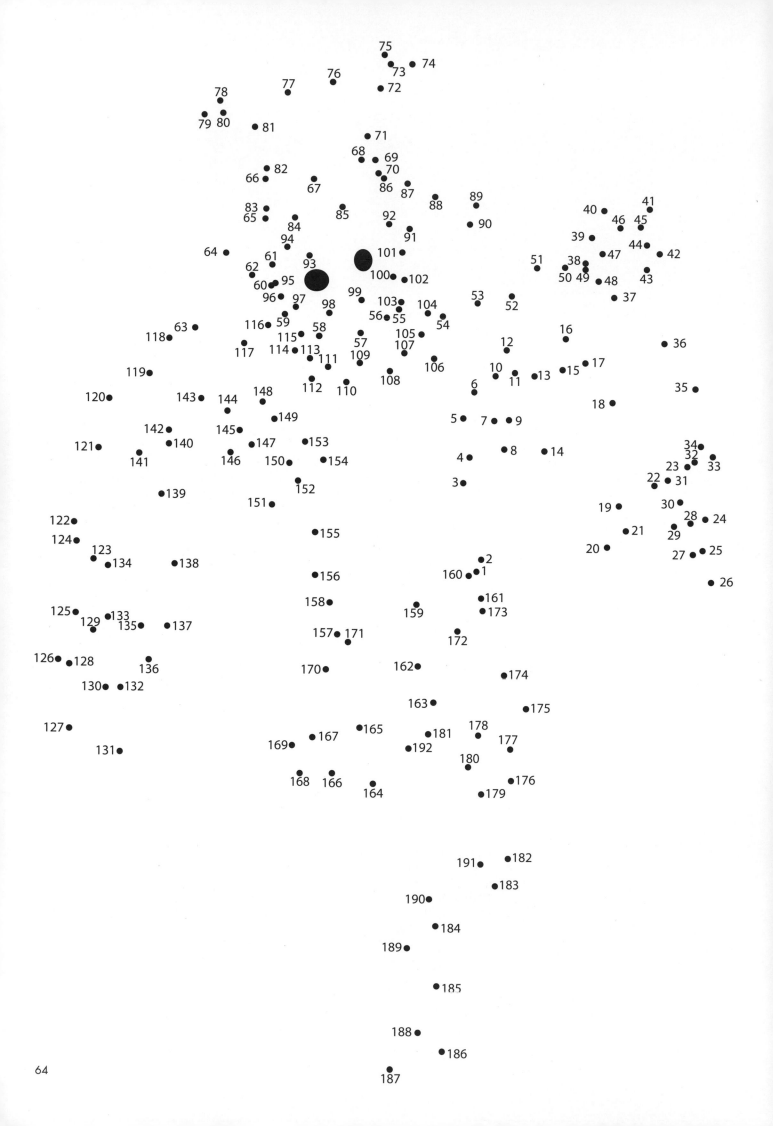

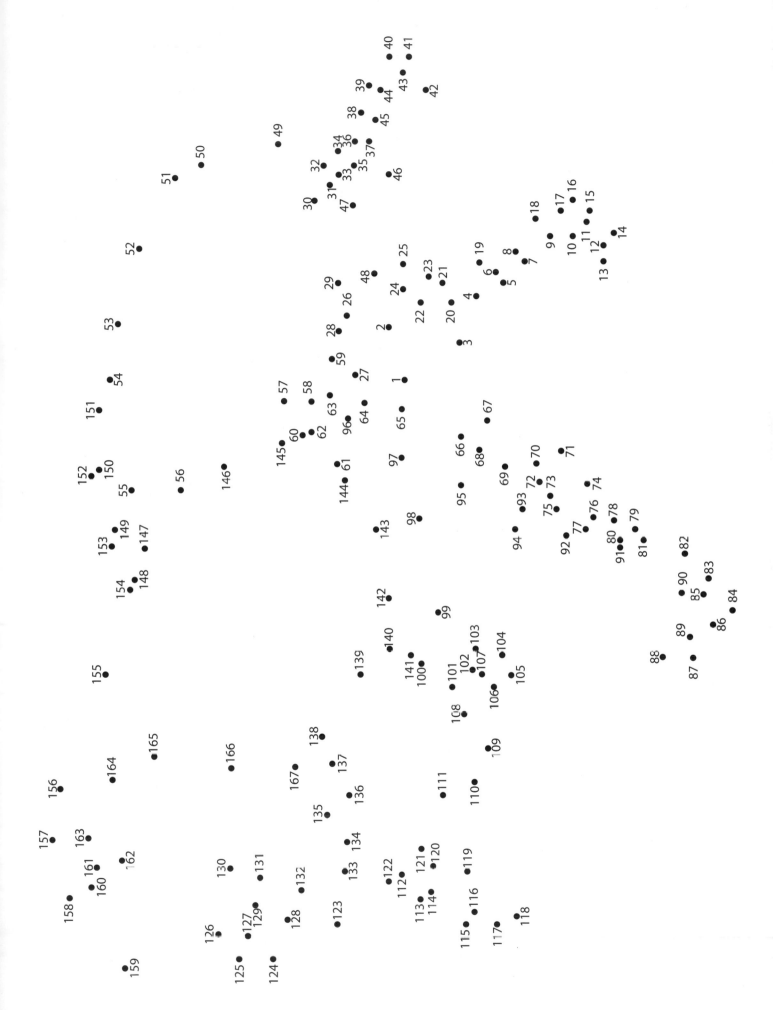

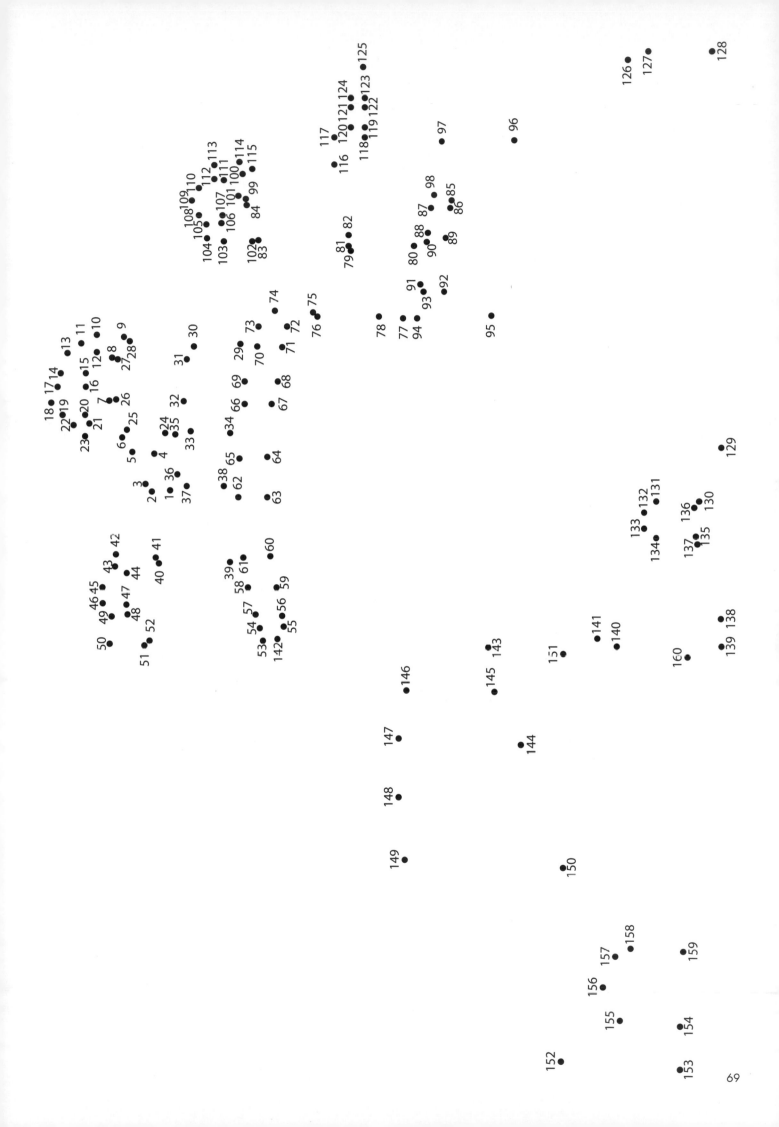

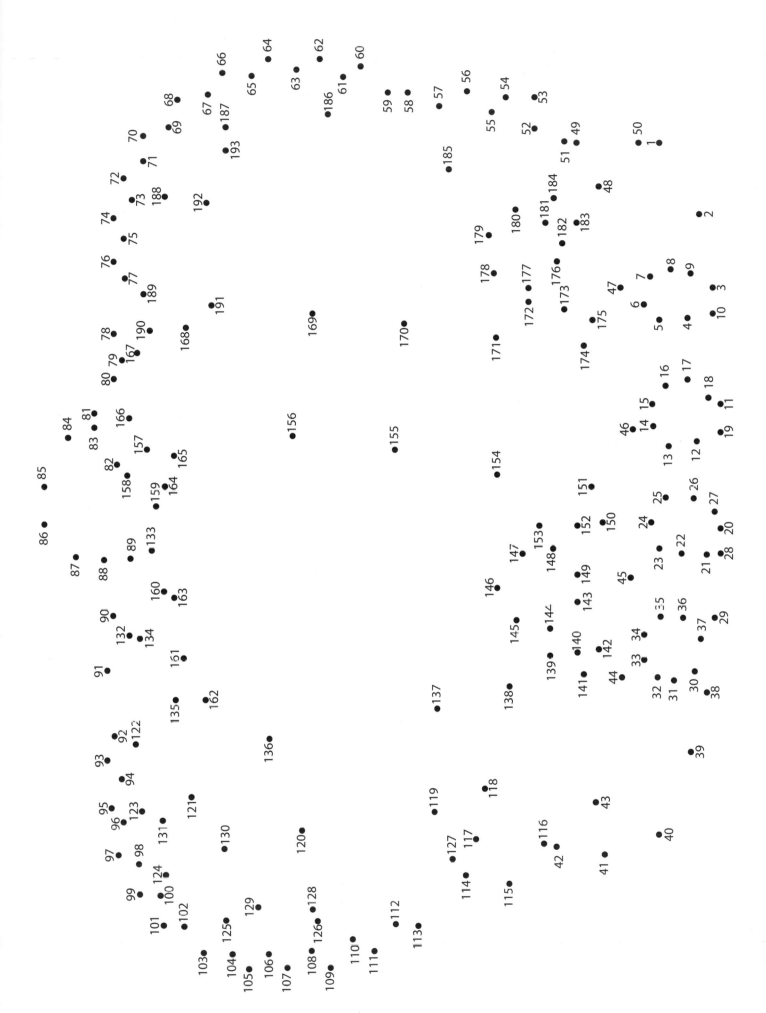

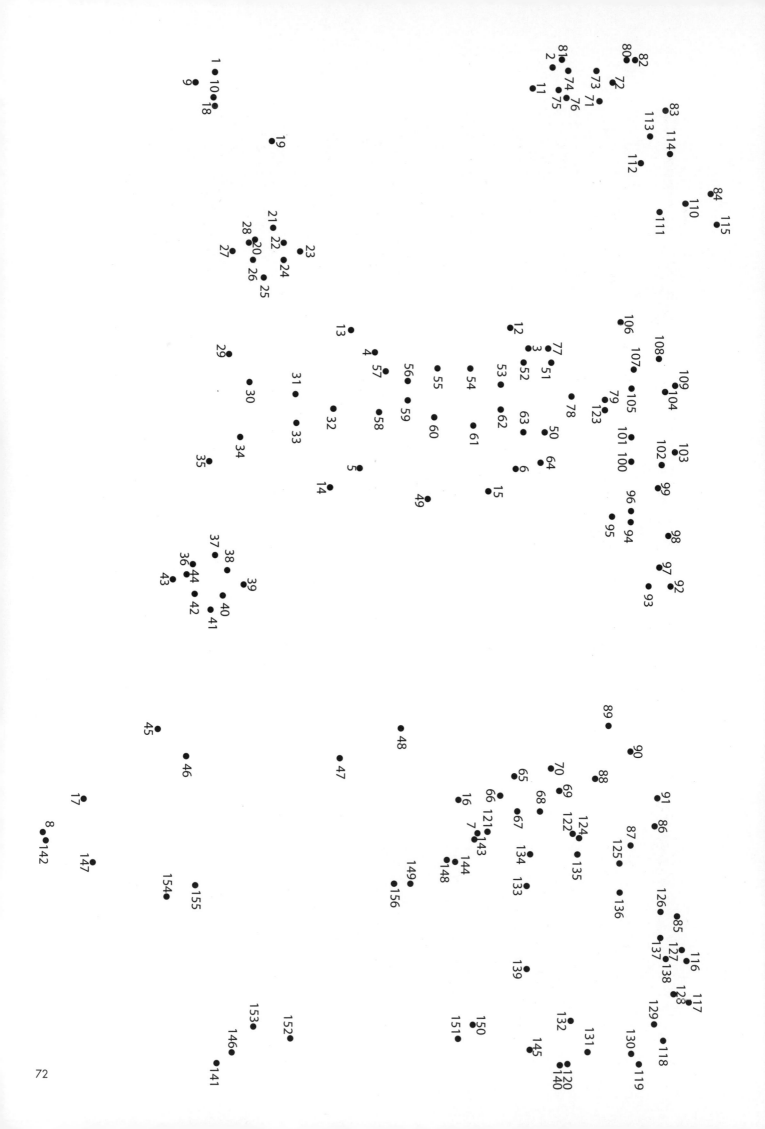

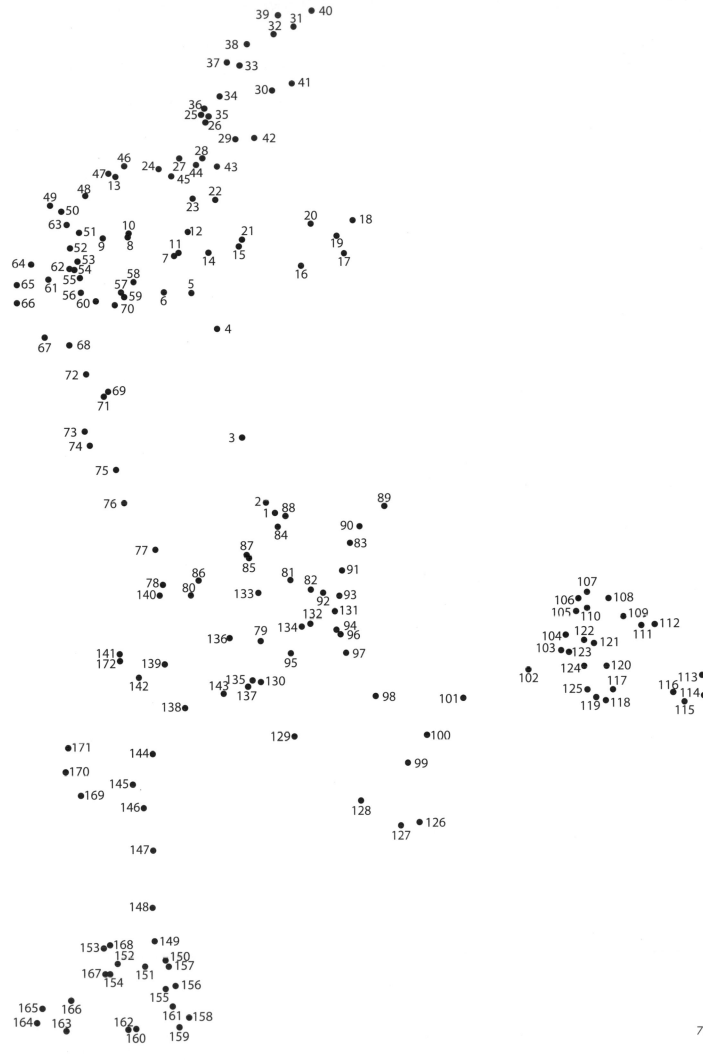

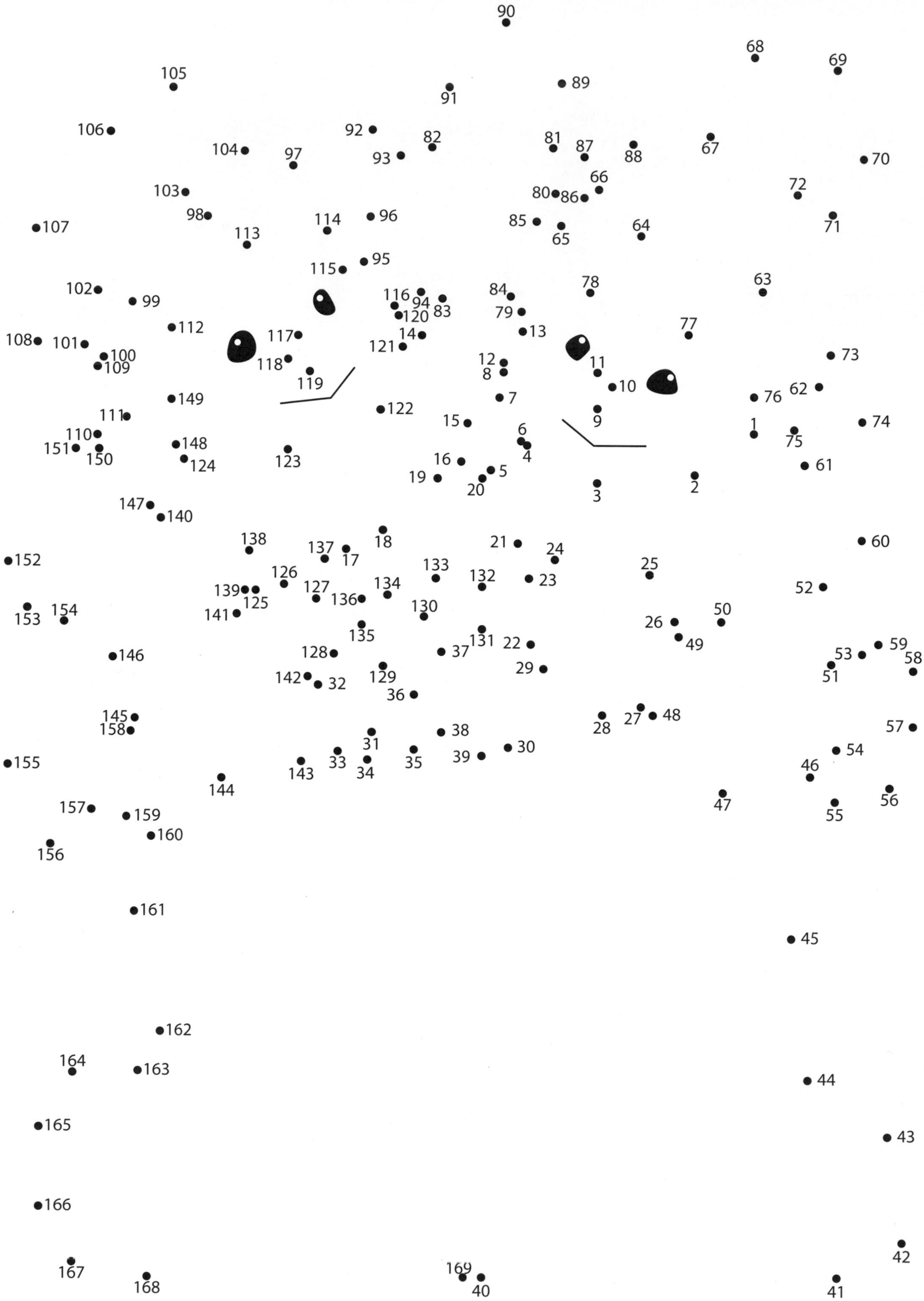

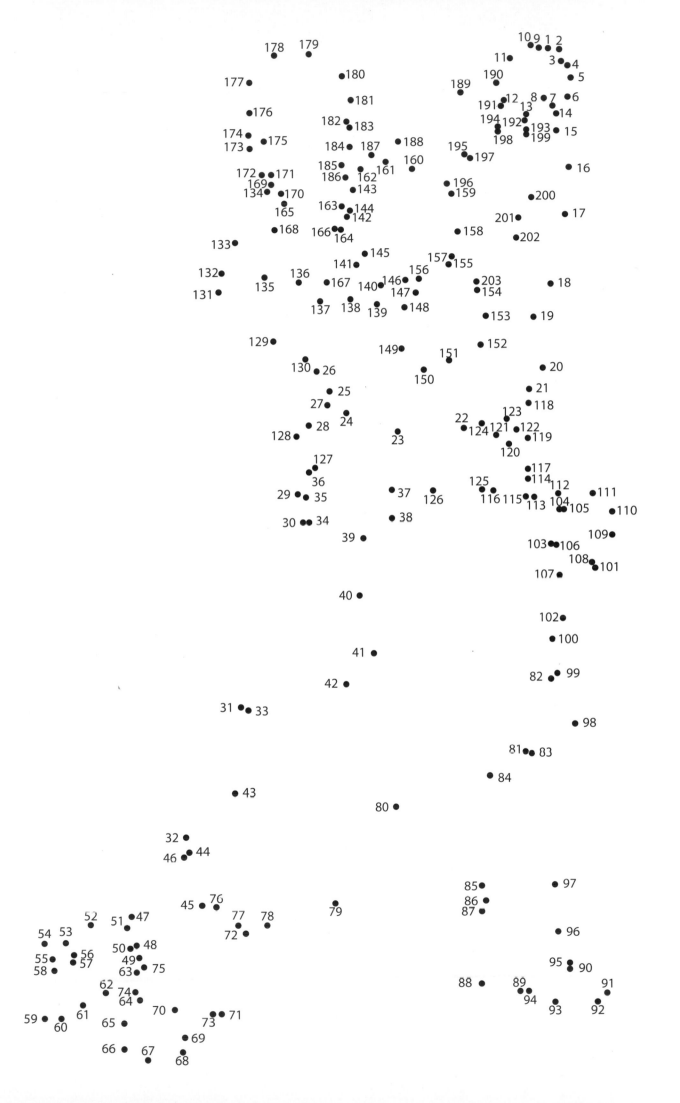

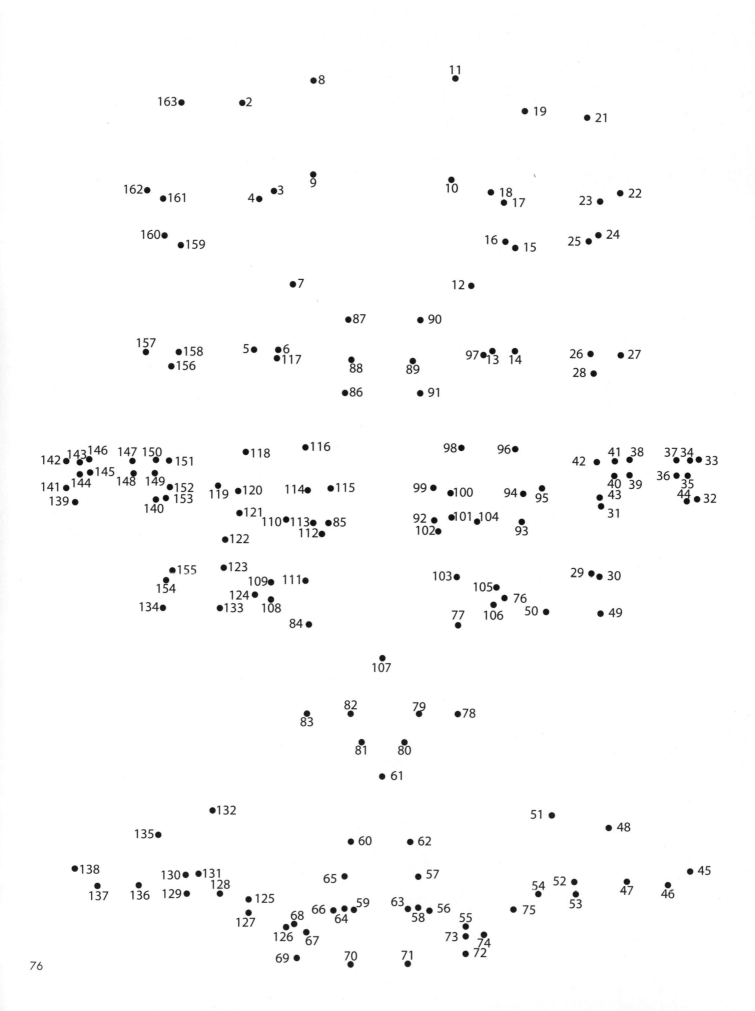

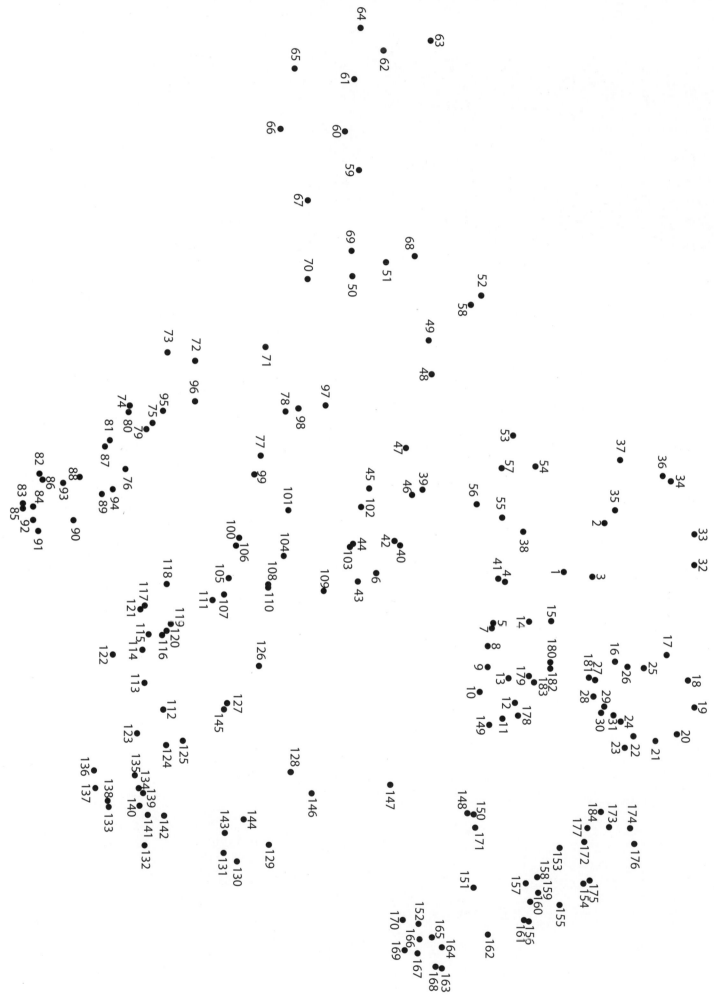

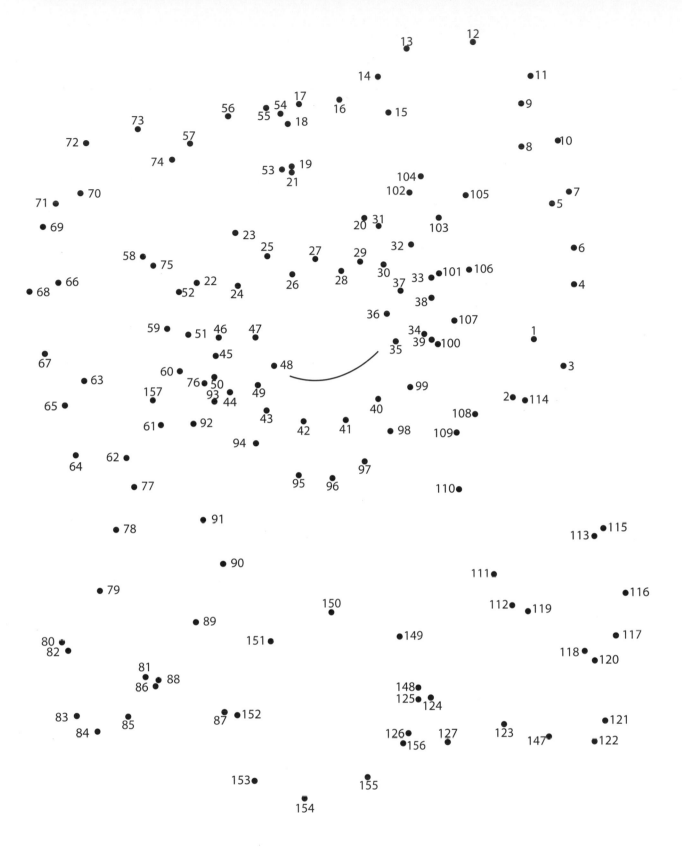

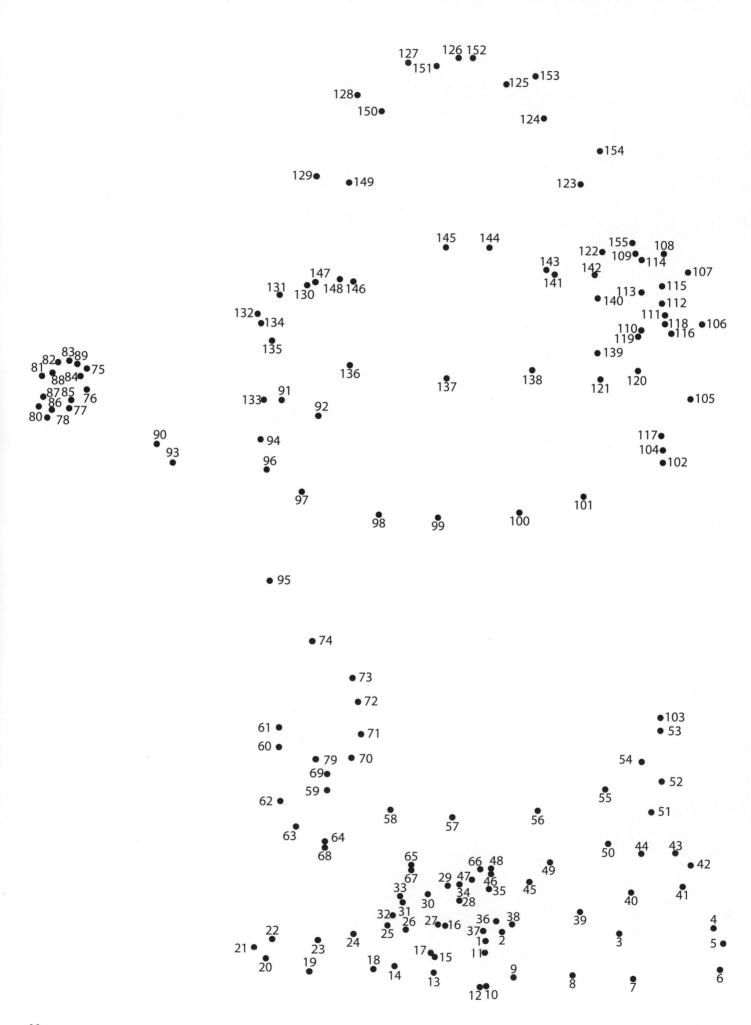

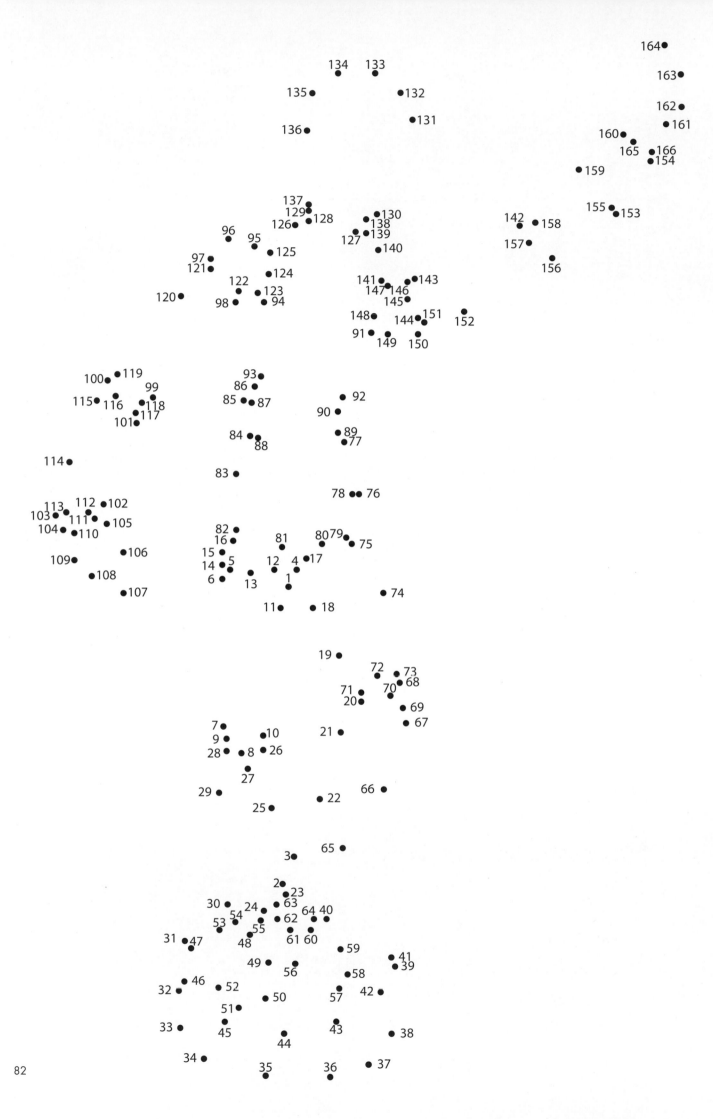

83

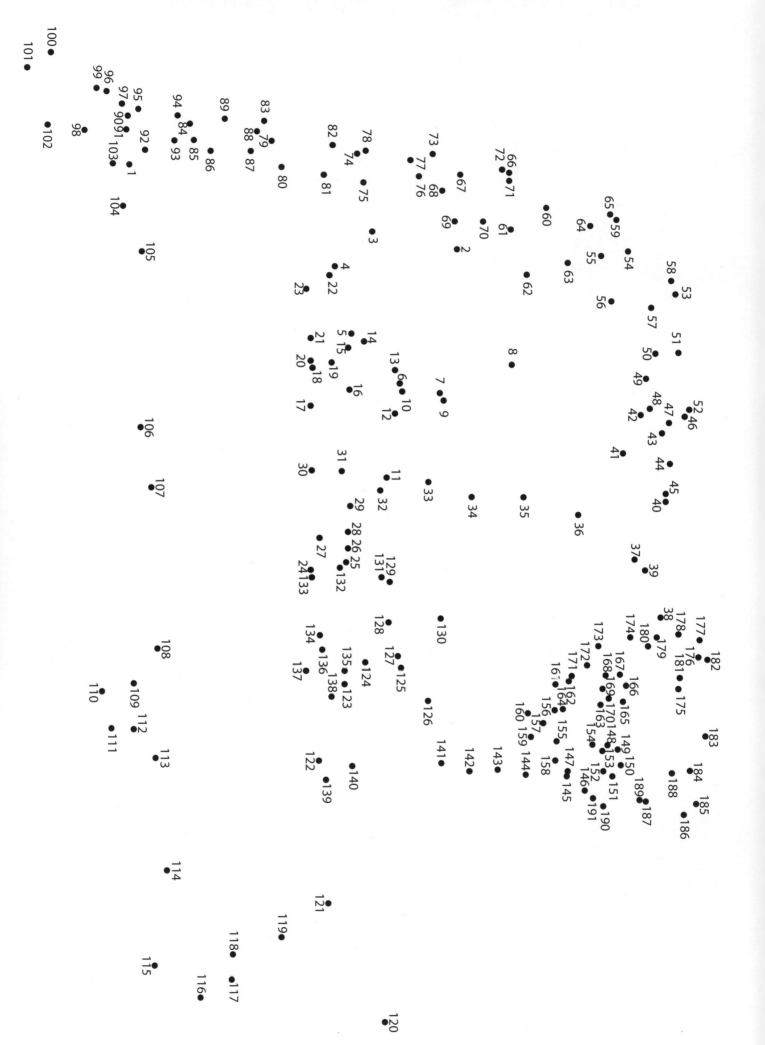

84

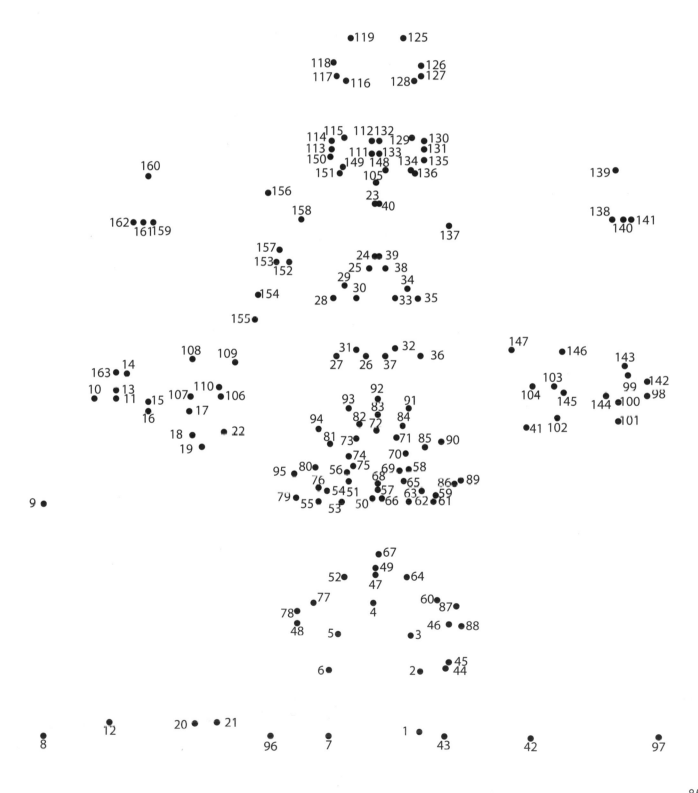

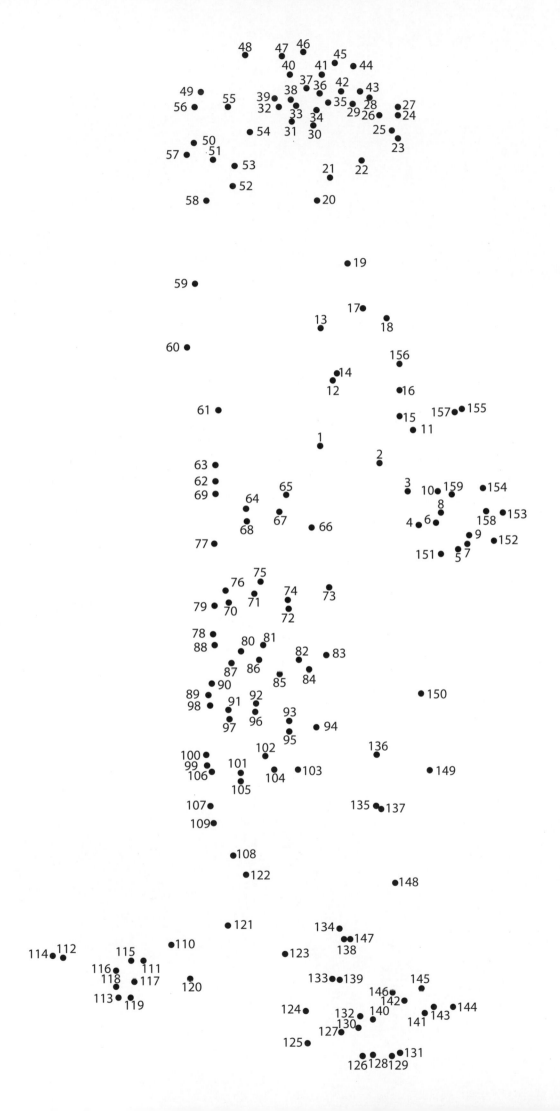

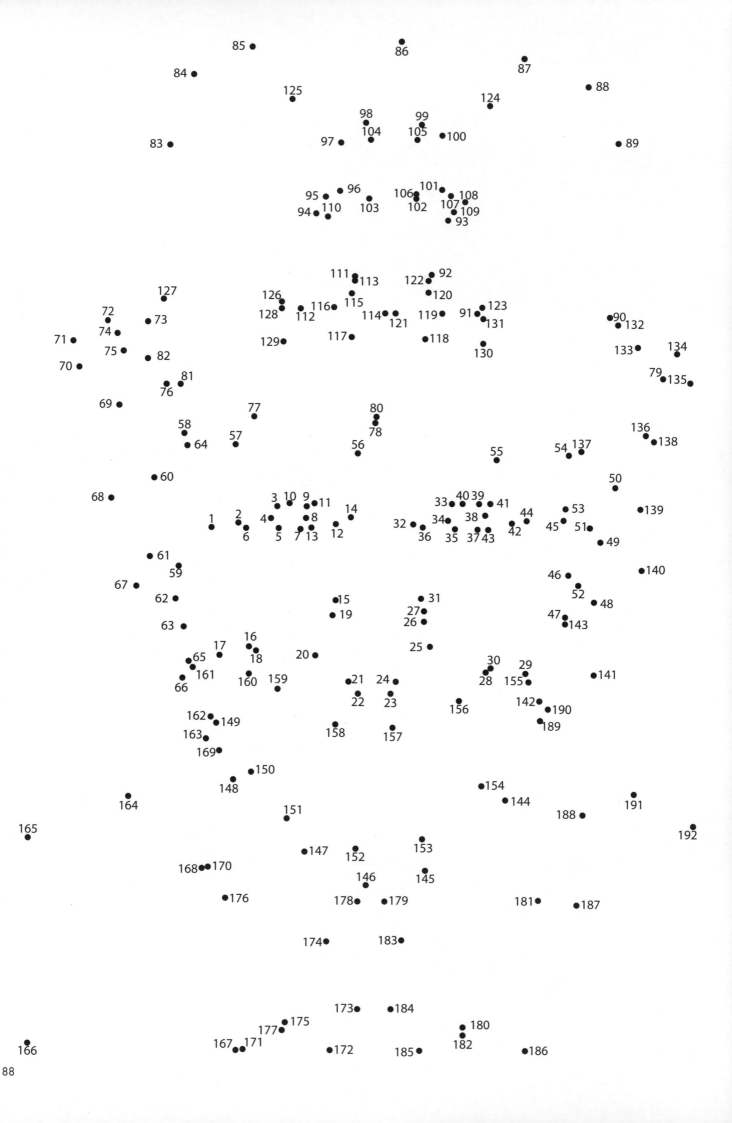

94

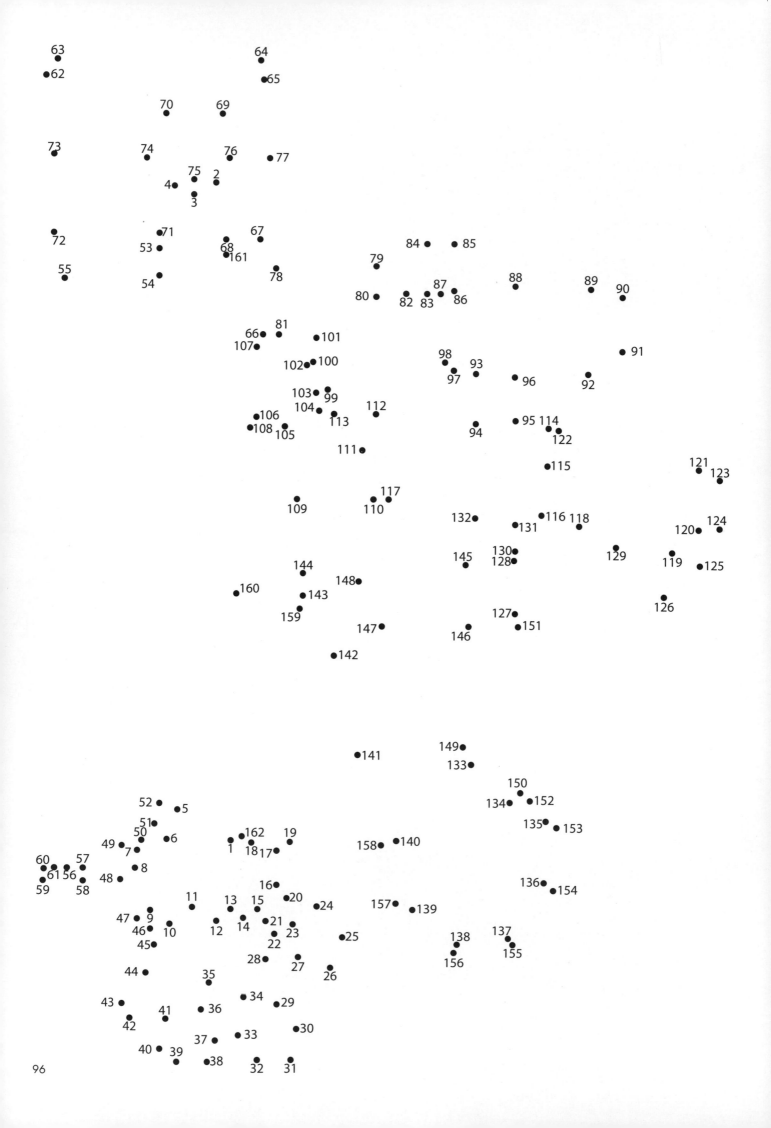

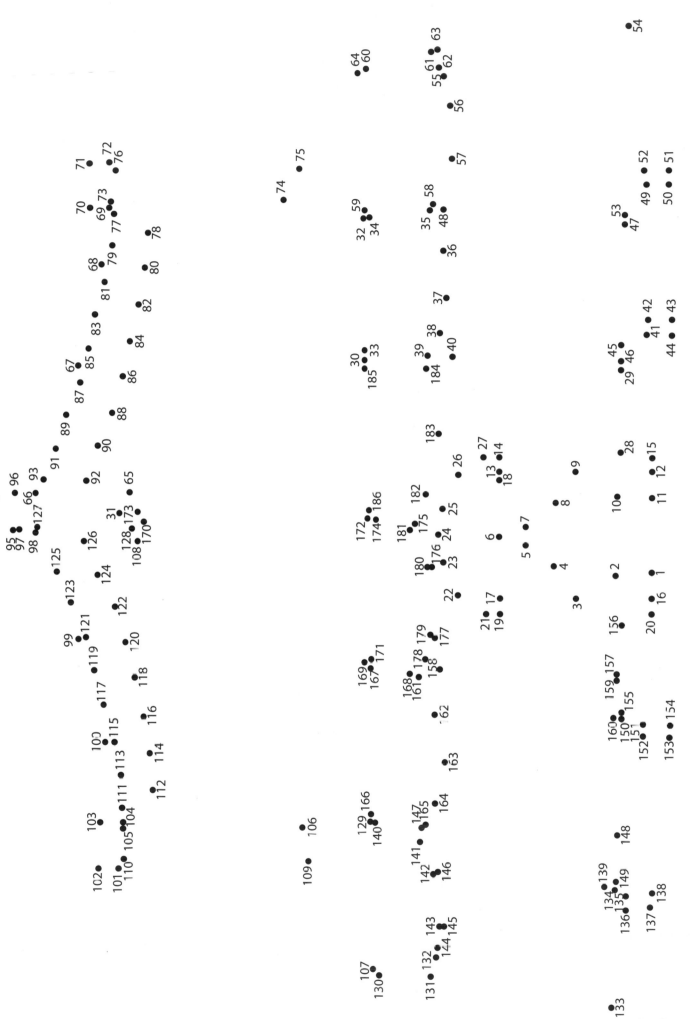

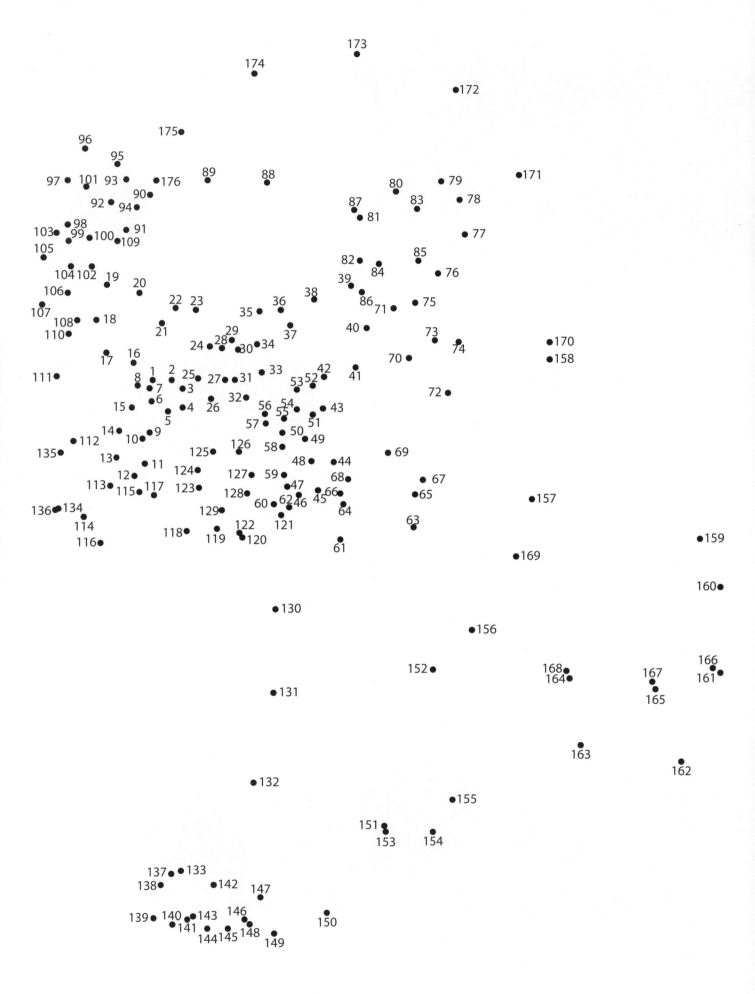

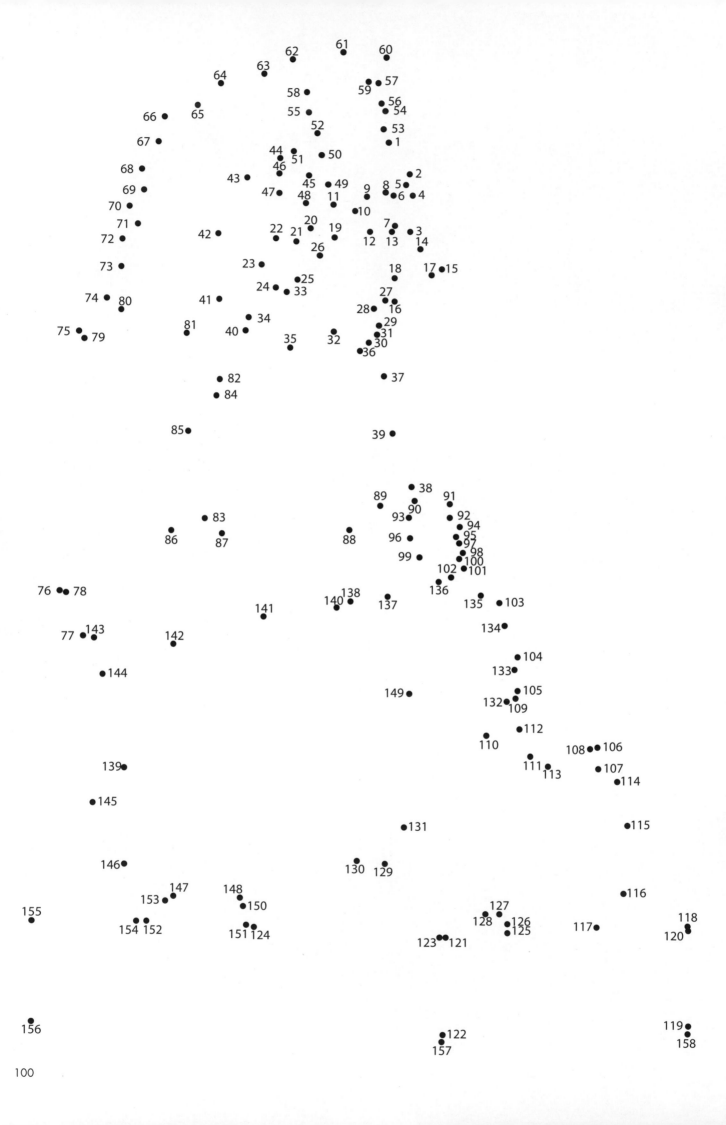

100

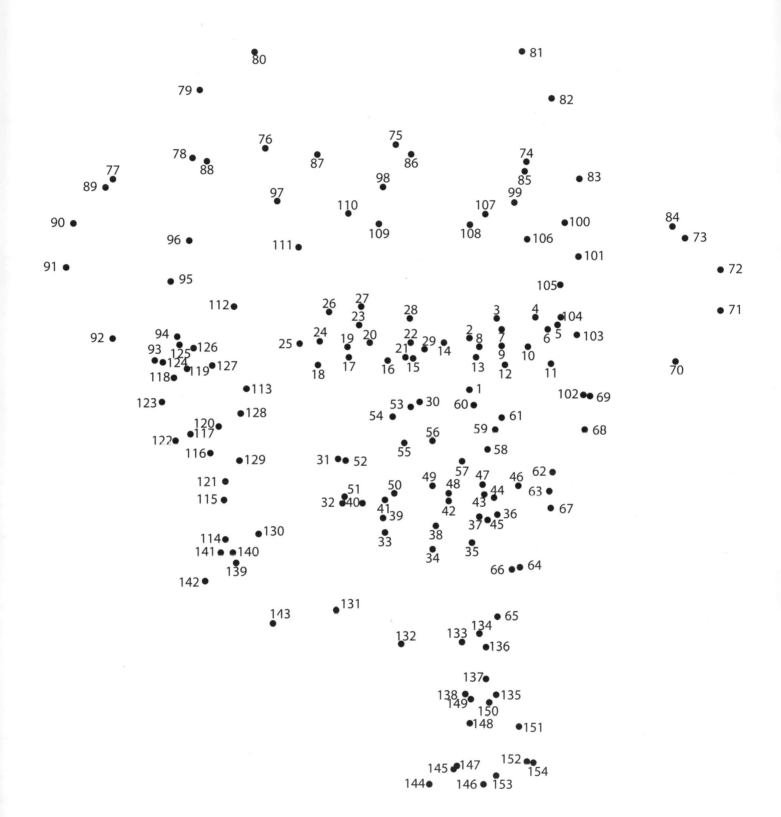

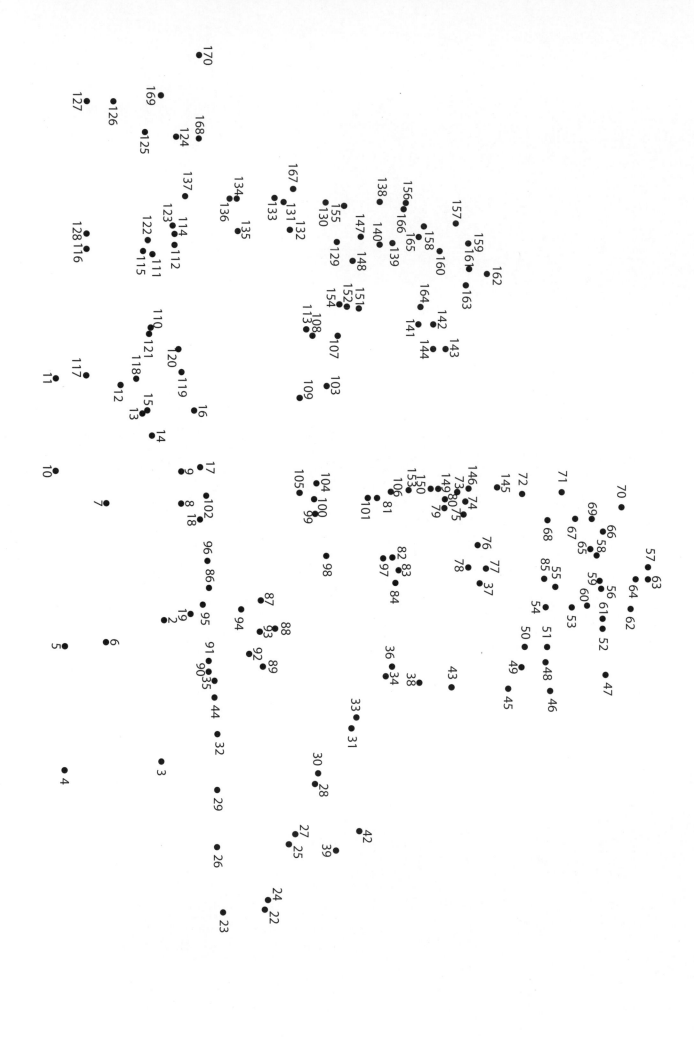

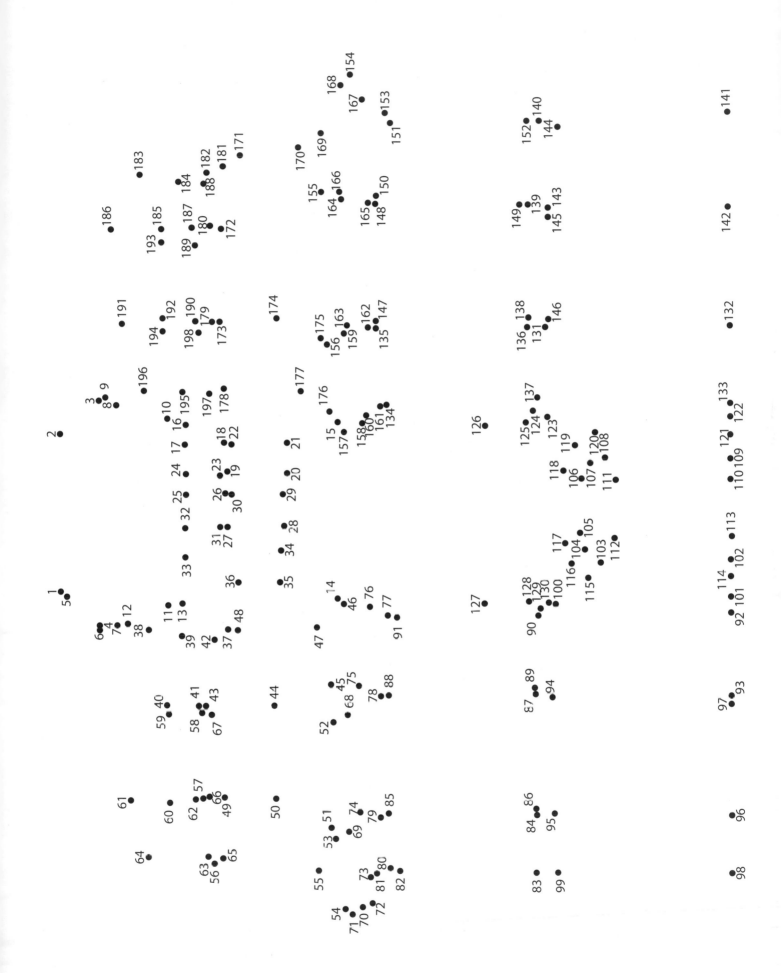

103

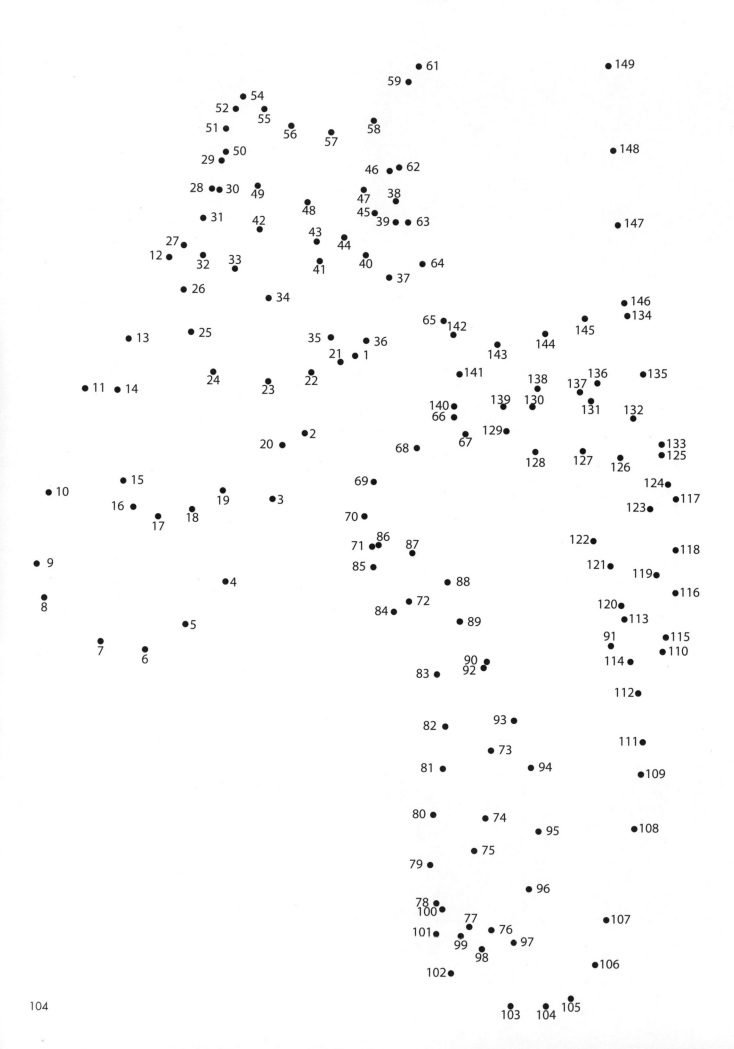

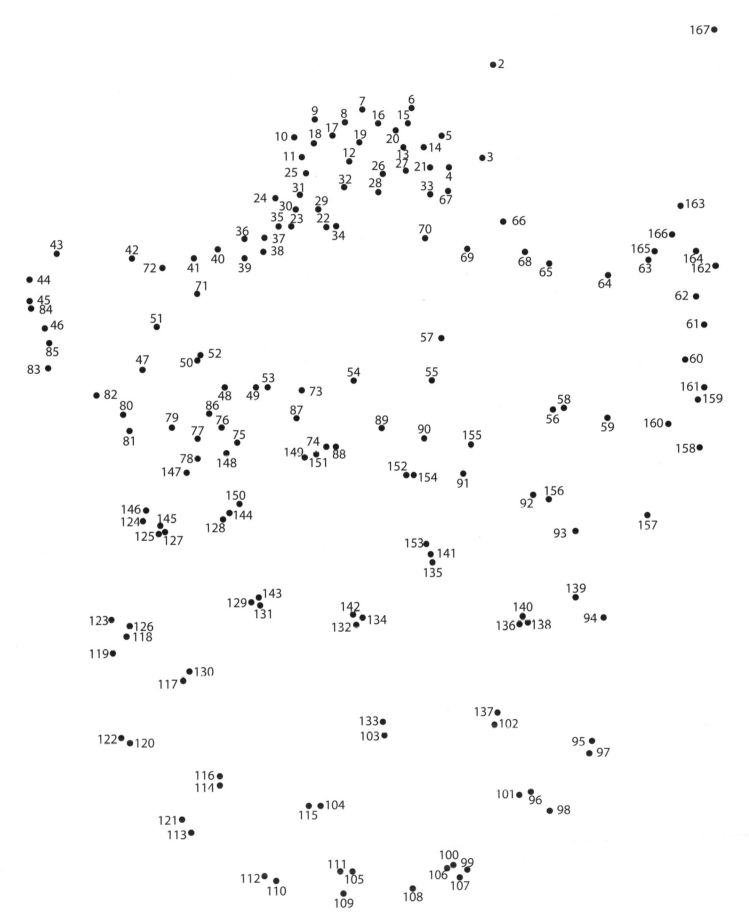

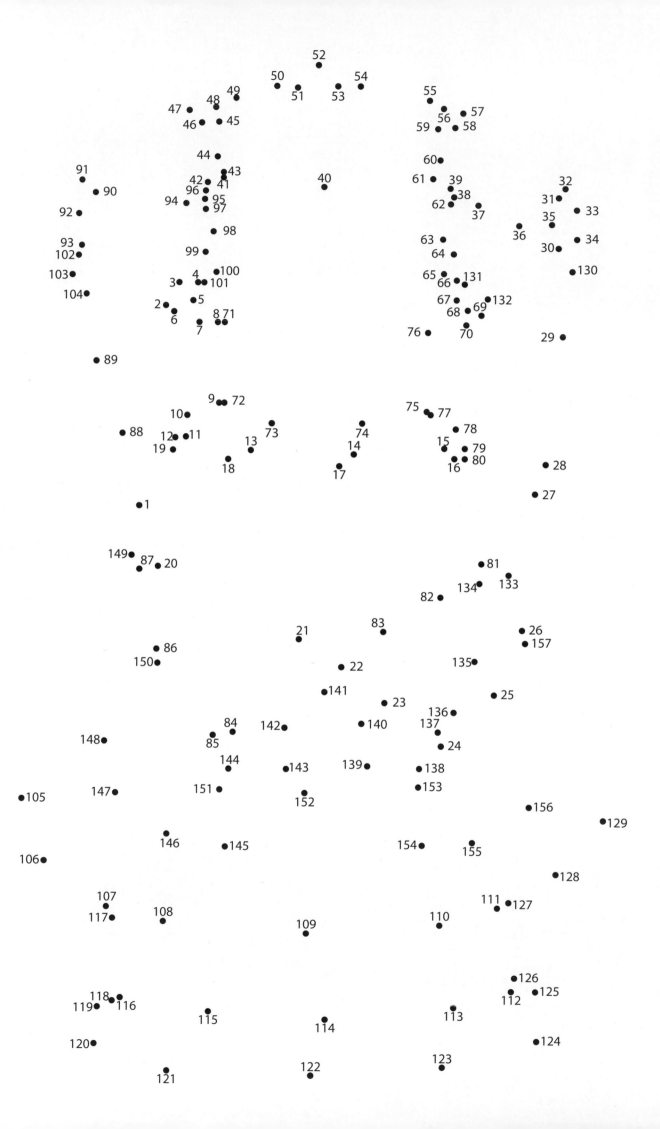

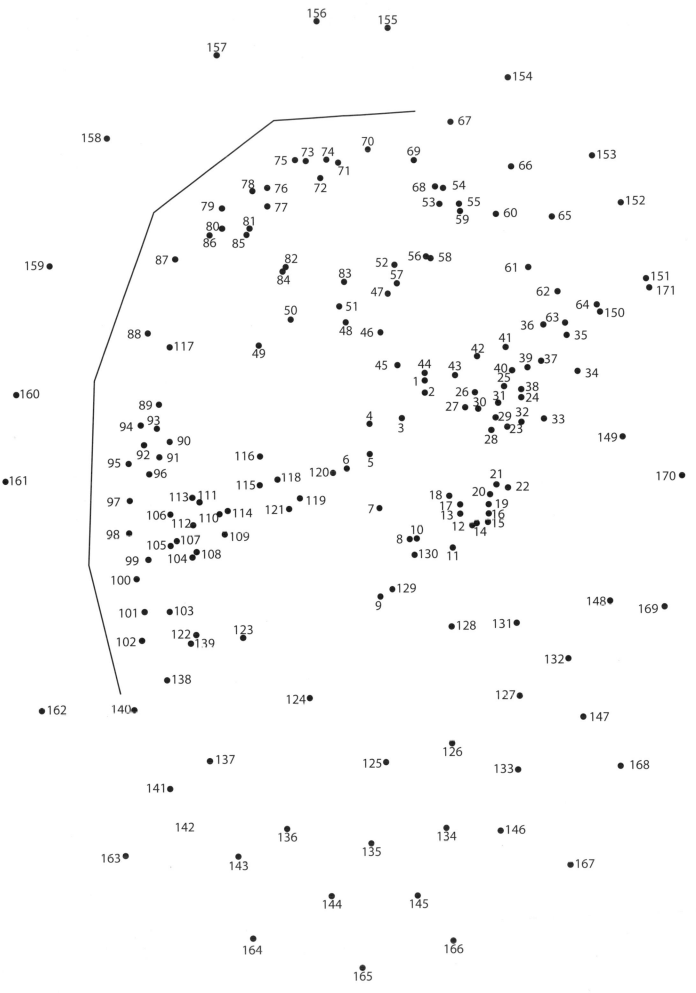

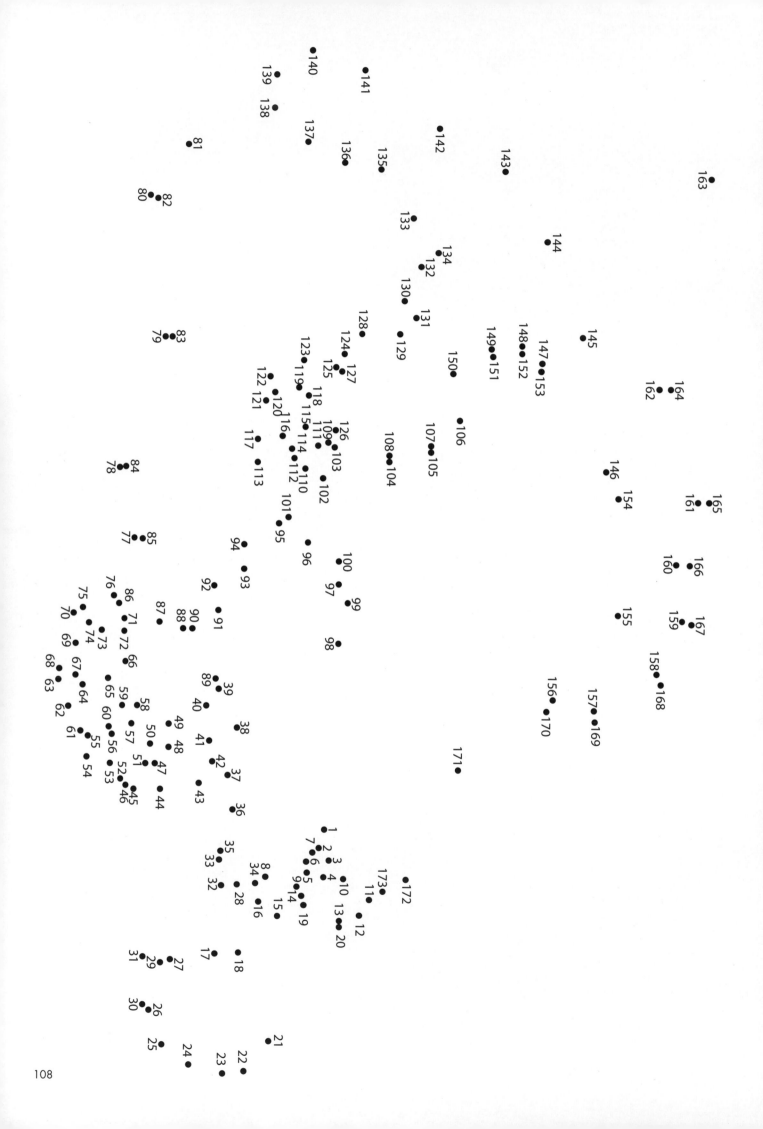

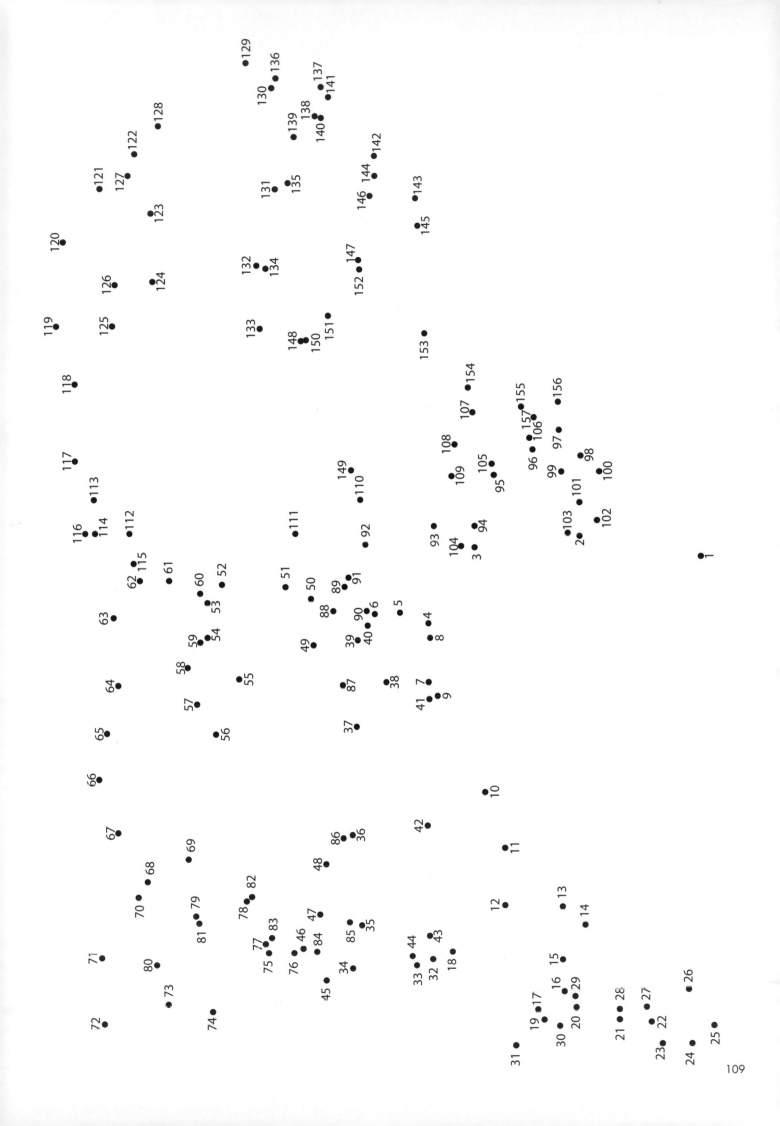

109

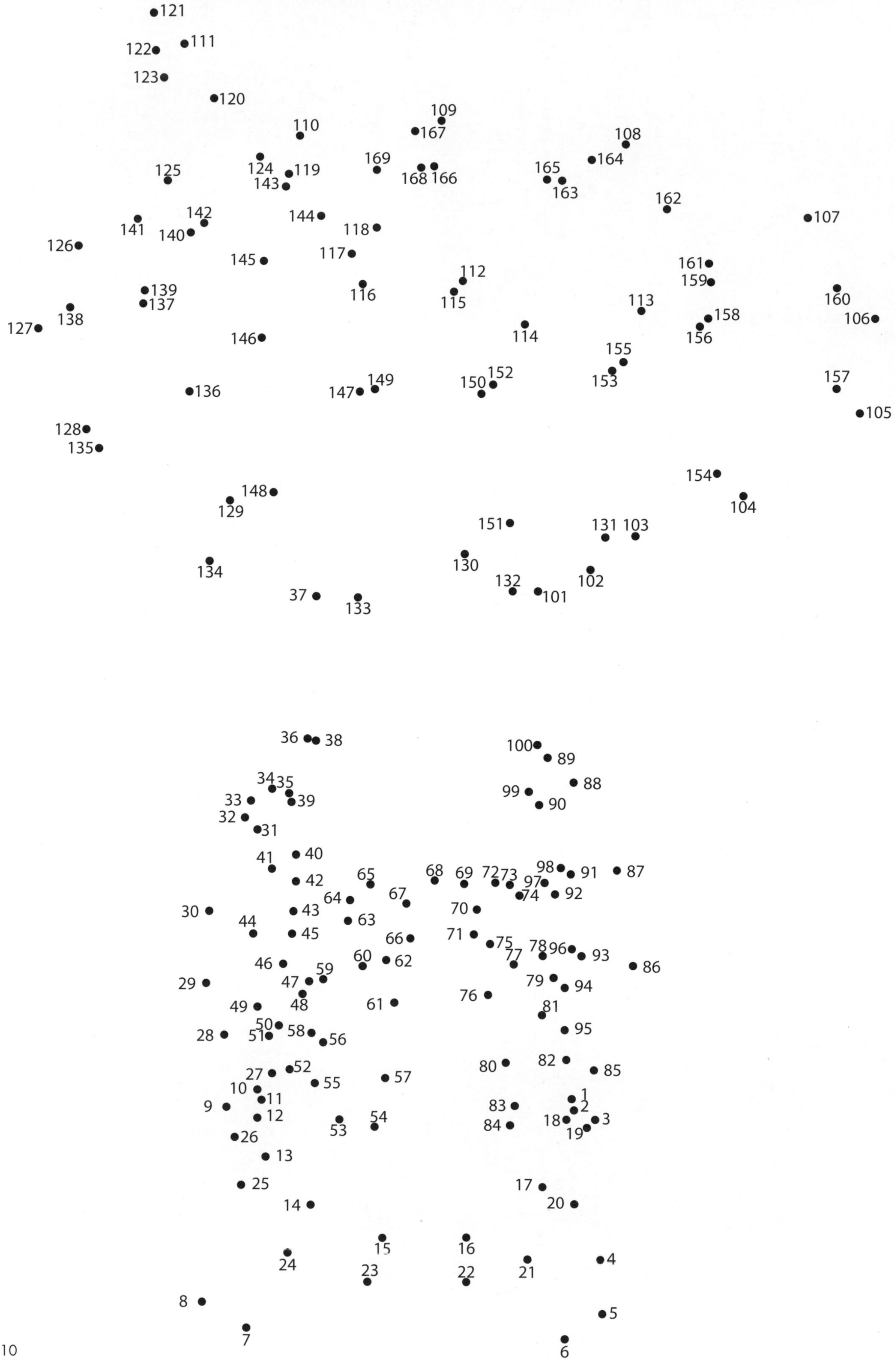

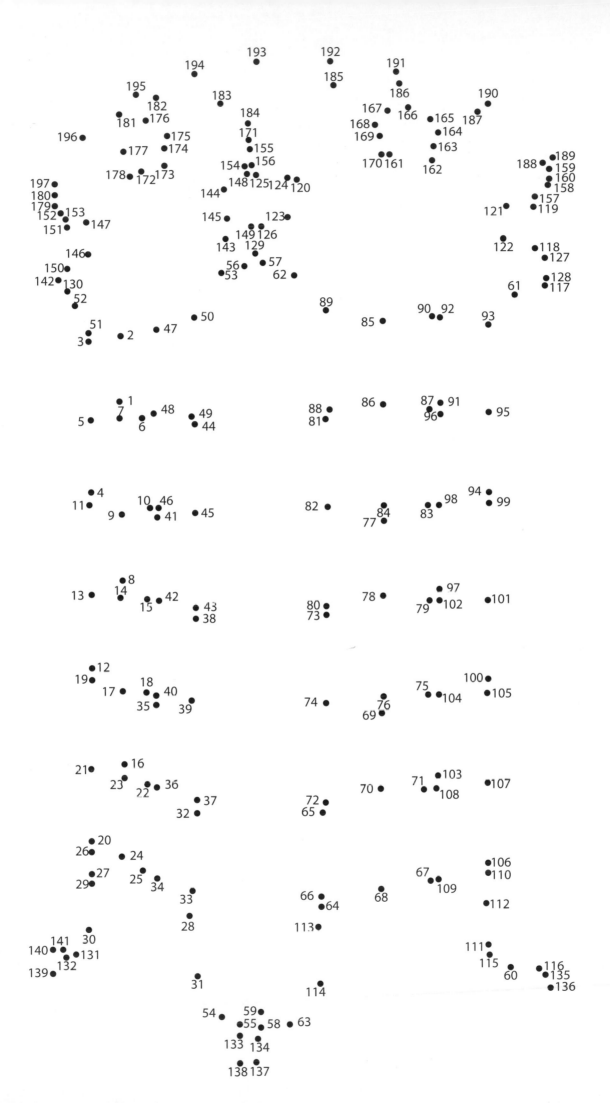

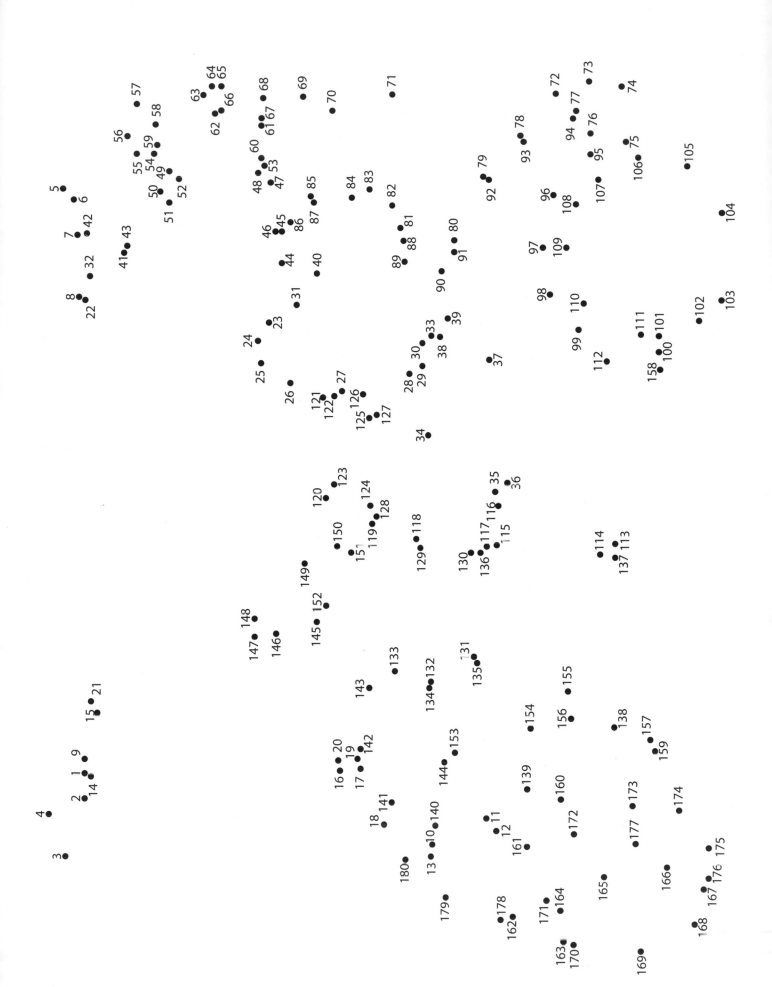

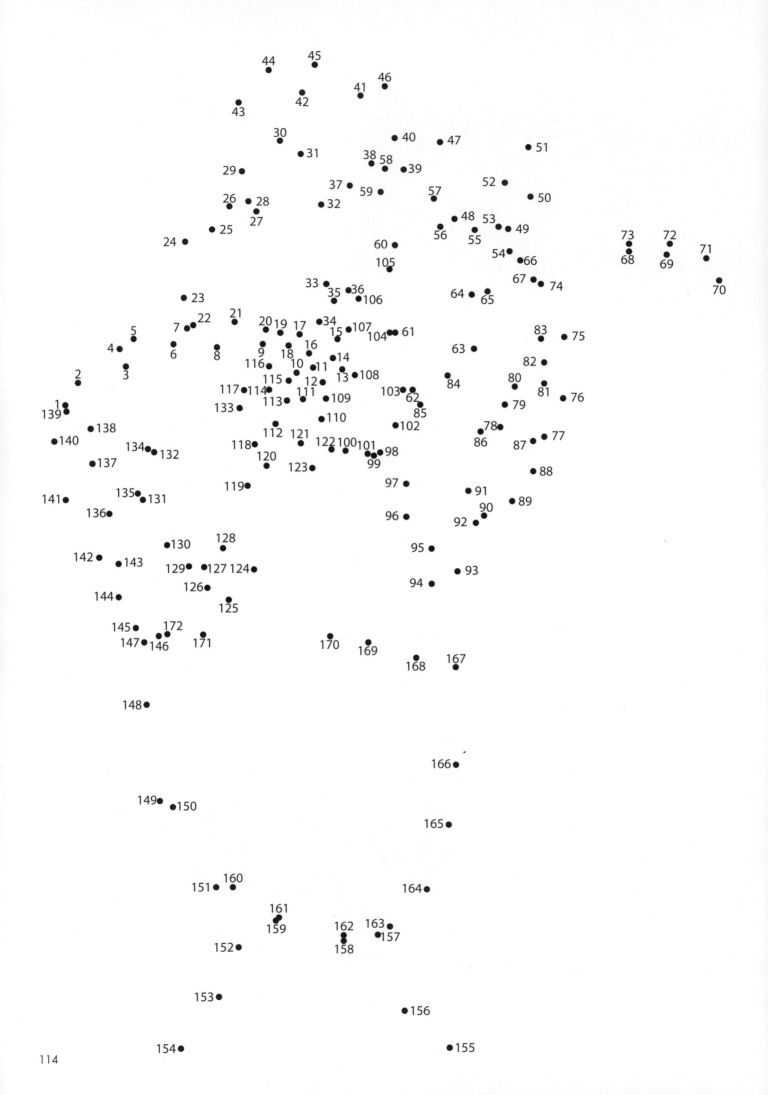

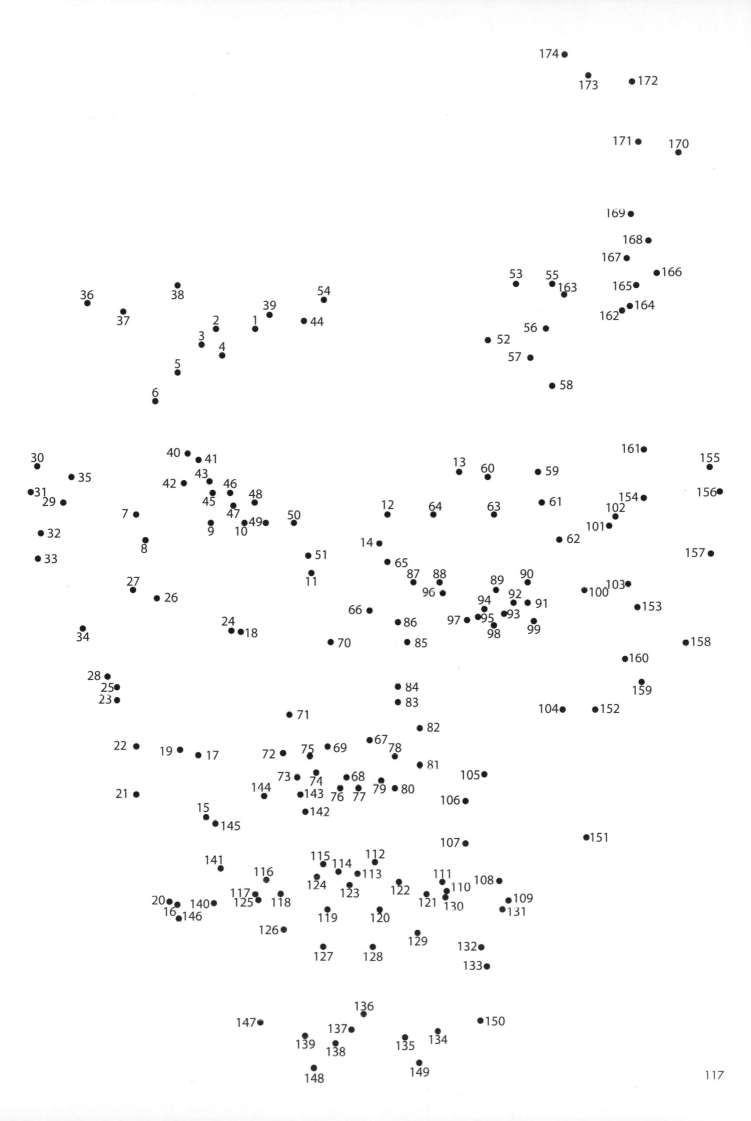

106● ●107

154●
108● ●153
103● 104●
105● 155●
102● 114● 110● 1●
115● 113● 109● 2●
116● 112● 150●
101● 111● 152● 151●

122● 123●
121● 124●
118● 140● 133● 149● 3●
100● 117● 125● 132●
119● 120● 135● 134● 126● 131● 148●
98● 99● 141● 127● 130●
142● 139● 136● 128●
97● 138137● 129●
147●
143● 146● 4●
96● 144● 145● 12●
11● ●10 13● 14●
5● 15●
19● 18● 16●
9● 17●
95● 20●
21●
8●
94● 6● 7●
76● 22●
23●
25●
93● 35● 24● 44●
92● 91● 28● 26● 50●
85● 27● 43●
84● 34● 36●
75● 77● 86● 90● 45● 51●
87● 49●
74● 83● 89● 33● 42●
82● 88● 46●
37● 48●
29● 52●
73● 78● 32● 41●
81● 47●
38● 53●
72● 79● 54●
80● 30● 40●
31● 55●
70● 39●
71● 69● 56●
68● 61● 58●
63● 57●
66● 64● 60●
67● 62● 59●
118
65●

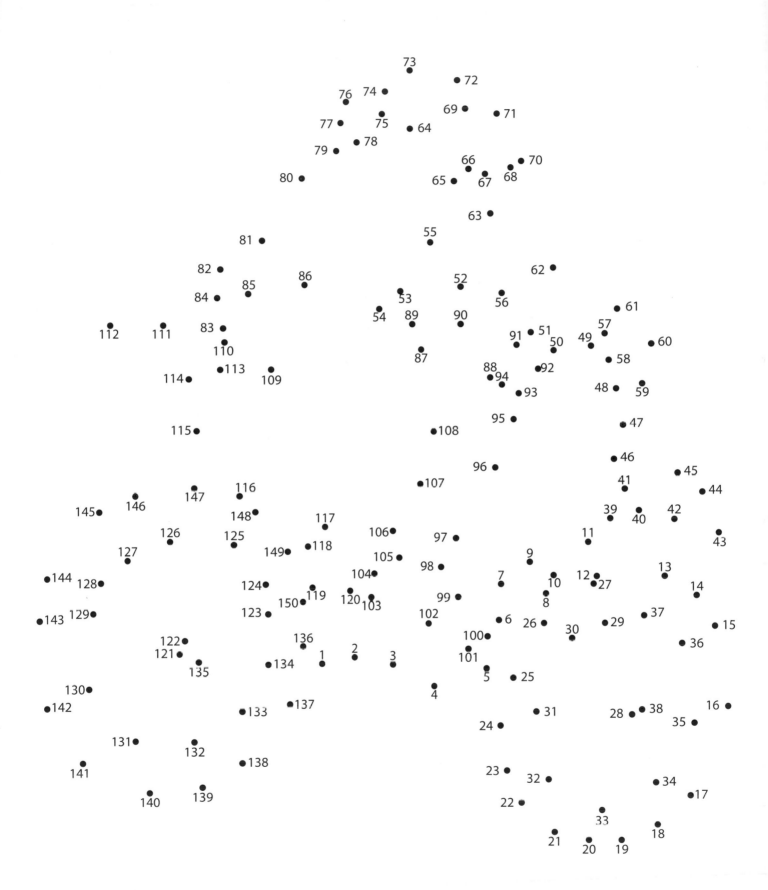

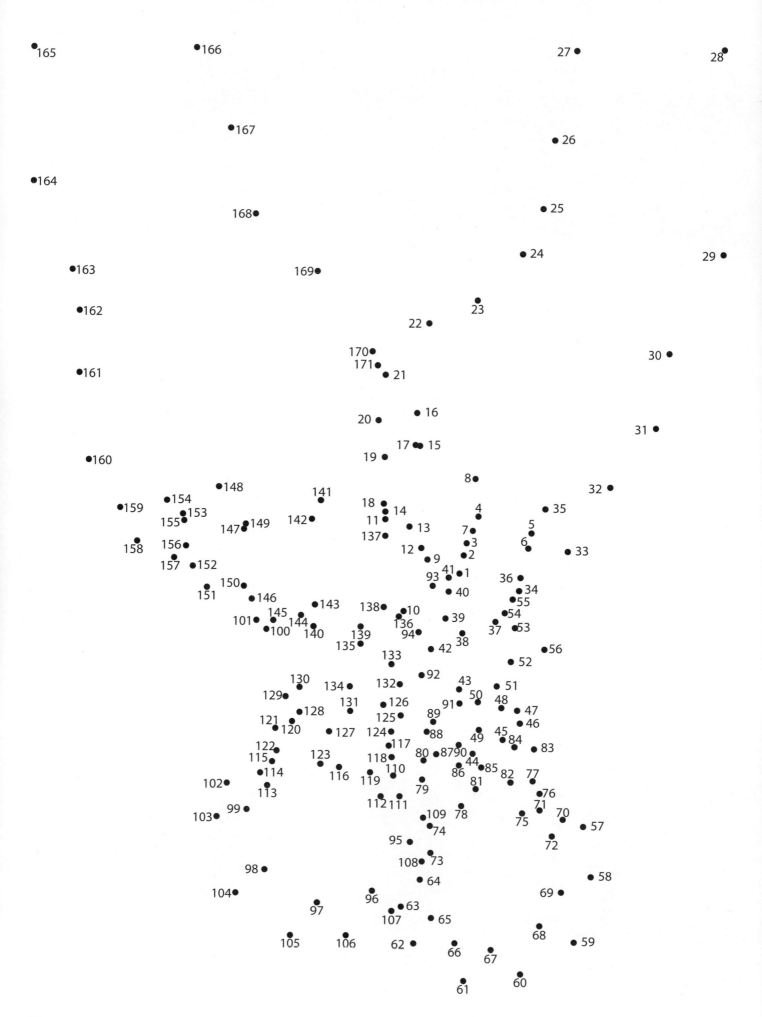

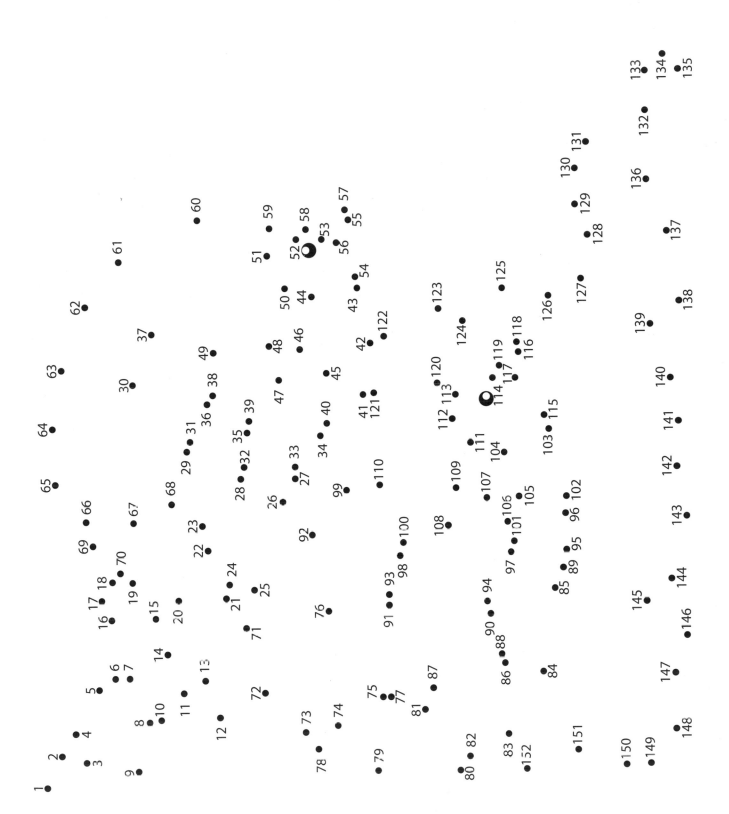

List of illustrations